D1188278

A Treasury of
French Tales

A Treasury of
French Tales

Newly
collected and told by
Henri Pourrat
Translated by Mary Mian
and illustrated by
Pauline Baynes

The Riverside Press Cambridge
HOUGHTON MIFFLIN COMPANY BOSTON
1954

Introduction

I WAS BORN AT AMBERT, in Lower Auvergne, in the Gallo-Roman times.

Actually, Auvergne in 1890 was antiquity, such as you would have found it in the days of the Greeks and the Latins when they were overflowing with malice, freshness, and sparkle. Antiquity, with its great men in quite small circles, whose peculiarities were noted, whose sayings and small talk were collected with care.

And I suppose that many of the tales are just that: a wonder, like that of Plutarch before some village worthy, who found such a good answer one day to an embarrassing question, or caught himself so cleverly when his foot slipped. Just as there are model lives, there are model sayings, those of the great and canny. Or those of the simple and innocent, which are almost as lovely and blessed in the sight of God.

Then there are tales with more thought in their making, more courtly tales, invented not in the farm-houses but in the castles or priories and convents; they found favour in the farm-houses and took root there. *The Tale of Count Robert* is one of these.

And more and more of them. They can be catalogued, category by category. They can be classified and explained, but it would lead nowhere. I believe that they came from everywhere and were made for everybody. May they now reach the hearts of English-speaking readers, with whom I am happy to join hands, thanks to this book.

v

In all these tales there spring up any number of sharp details, reminders of the world of fields and woods, like that of the fables of La Fontaine. And if the tales are what they should be, they have a certain twist that helps them to loop the loop in the air of time.

Because of these details, this twist, and because of a secret breath within, perhaps, the tales at times become something different—that is, they themselves become characters.

And so they fit into the kingdom of shepherdesses, close-cropped pastures where great violets spring up, at the foot of windy heights where there is only a castle of round rocks and three mountain ash trees, and far away a ribbon of blue mountains that winds away to the end of the world.

These tales are a childhood. The first requisite is to report them faithfully. You are lucky when you can write them down at the dictation of a story-teller with the gift. But when they come to you all flattened out and dried up, you must try to give them back life and sap, by letting them recover their freshness at the fountain welling in the grass. The problem, and a hard one it is, is to add nothing, unless it be touches drawn from the great popular imagination of songs and proverbs. You should tell them just as would have done the most gifted of the shepherdesses. In such a way that through them your listeners can smell the pastures, the violets, the round rocks, and even that far-off blue like the fringe of heaven. And so that they will long to go there themselves, to find the country of happiness, that promised land.

For that land, in the end, is what it is all about. Perhaps it is just this literature of every day that deals most often with the means of reaching it. Many tales seem to have no other purpose than to teach you how to get along in the world, how to find the right word to say, the thing to do—*The Two Millers and the Charcoal-Burner*, *The Devil and the Peasant*, *The Well-Salted Soup*, *Saint Peter's Chicken*—or to invent good

Introduction

humour, courage, humility, thrift, human tenderness—*The Grain of Wheat, The Nail, Belle-Rose, The Lady and the Hind.* But there are others, the richest, boldest, and most fanciful, that mean still more than this—*The Singing Branch, The Little Frog, Vidal, The Boat that Sailed on Land.* These are incantations. They try, with an utter freedom of imagination, to have everything. Here is a ragged boy, with cracks in his sabots and holes in his pockets: tomorrow he will have everything—the pot full of heavy gold pieces, the castle with twelve towers at the end of an avenue of oaks, and, more radiant than the stars, the beautiful princess, the king's daughter.

Other men were satisfied with timid magics; they scratched upon a bone or painted on a rock the game they hoped to make their own in the hunt. As he sat by the red fire on which he threw dead branches and tufts of broom and watched the flames spring up, the story-teller imagined everything—boats that allowed you to go faster than the wind, chariots that went all by themselves still faster, or flew through the air like a falcon, words that sped in an instant from one end of the world to the other—in short, all the marvels which today man has at his sorry disposal. Moonstruck imagination has succeeded at last. All that is lacking is happiness, but that will come this year or the next —it is just around the corner.

The tales, especially those that go deepest, are simply this: each one of them cries out to the sons of the earth that it is high time to be happy. That is the end of all incantations invented by man, as soon as he domesticated fire and began to practise his trades and his arts.

Did I say the Gallo-Roman times? I might as well confess it now—I was born at Ambert, in Auvergne, in the Age of Chipped Stone—no, let's not exaggerate: of Polished Stone.

HENRI POURRAT

AMBERT, 1953

vii

Contents

A Treasury of French Tales

*A Treasury of
French Tales*

The Tale of the
Three Skilful Sons

ONCE UPON A TIME there was a man who was a carpenter by trade and so clever that he could have made eyes for a cat. He had, however, one regret: that in the days of his youth he had never travelled the roads of France, staff in hand and wearing the colours of his trade, like a master-workman. 'They say that anything I turn my hand to is well done. But, if only I had learned from the masters, then I'd have shown them something!'

But he had never left his own village. When evening came, he sat on his doorstep, smoking his pipe, looking off down the road as it wound away like a ribbon. Down the hill it led, towards all of France: towards villages terraced on the hillside, with the tower of a church rising above them: towards heights and towns far away, brilliant as those you see through a glass of water: towards serene blue distances at the edge of the world. He thought of all that men have learned upon earth, of those who have the secrets and the trick of

I

the hand, either learned from the finest master or stumbled upon by luck. And once more he said to himself that it was a pity, when you are young and need only good legs and a good will, not to set forth and learn all that the great blue world has to teach you.

This carpenter had three sons. When they had come of age, he told them:

'He who knows all the tricks of his trade, who sings as he works, and works as well as the finest master of them all— well, he is a man. My boys, you must be off now, to travel the roads of France. Come back in seven years to the day. And to him who has become the cleverest with his hands, I shall give my house. There it is, I have said it!'

And the house was worth having, with its vine over the door, its garden, its peach-trees on the terrace, and the view it overlooked. When you saw it, set high over the town, you thought how much you would like to live there, and work with a joyful heart.

The three boys made their bundle and buckled their gaiters. Then they kissed father and mother, and took to the road.

Month by month, seven years went by. The father thought of them every evening, sitting on his doorstep. He looked out at the world spread before him: the towns scattered like white pebbles, the dance of the hills, and all that far-away blue. He thought of good comrades met by chance, in workshops, by the roadside, in city streets, and of the unbelievable things that a master can do by the skill of his hand. It is a great thing to have the wit that understands processes and sets them in motion. When his boys came back, would they have hands so clever that they seemed to think for themselves? Or would they be nothing but bunglers, clumsy fools who needed more than three strokes of a hammer to drive in a nail?

One July evening, seven years to the day after their leaving, the three boys came back—all three together. One was a master-at-arms, the second a blacksmith, and the third a cook.

'Now then, boys, show us what you have learned to do. Remember—the house goes to the cleverest.'

'Oh, my brothers have gone far beyond me!' said the cook modestly.

'We'll know that when we have tasted your cooking,' said the father. 'To celebrate your home-coming, why not make us a mushroom omelet?'

'Mushrooms?' said the cook. 'Very well! I'll go and pick them in the woods on the hillside.'

'We'll go with you,' said the two others. And the father too; he couldn't let them out of his sight that evening.

The four of them had not yet crossed the vineyard when they saw a storm coming, and from the bad side of the sky. Castles of clouds piled up, the grey hiding the white; thunder rolled its tumbrils. Then another and more terrifying noise—hail.

No more use for baskets: the grapes were done for.

But when the first hailstone came spanking down, the master-at-arms snatched up a stake, forgotten in a corner, and with this wooden rapier in his hand, began to fence against the falling stones. The stake whirled about, stroke upon stroke, circle upon circle. The fellow darted here and there, left to right; his stake flew everywhere at once. He performed the tricks which men of his trade call the covered rose, the false sun. . . . His father, his brothers, were covered as by a roof, and so were his father's vines. Hailstones went on falling thick and fast: one didn't wait for the other. What a peppering! And yet he, with his furious stake, stopped them all in mid-air. What a steam he raised!

The storm passed on: peace was restored. Not a grape was touched, not a leaf.

'For a job, that's a job!' said the father, dumbfounded. 'The house will be yours, I'm thinking.'

'Wait till you see my brothers at work,' answered the master-at-arms, tucking his shirt-tails into his breeches.

At these words, just as they reached the road, they heard a horseman arriving at a gallop.

'His horse has lost the shoe off his forefoot,' said the blacksmith, pricking up his ears.

He went into the smithy at the foot of the hill, took a horseshoe, and set it on the fire. When the horse came up at break-neck speed, from the doorway the smith threw the horseshoe at him. The shoe stuck on his hoof, and stayed there. The horse had not even slackened his pace.

The father, as amazed as he had been at the master-at-arms, couldn't believe his eyes.

They went on to the grove, picked the mushrooms under the clumps of oak trees, and came back. The cook went to the hen-coop, and took the eggs he found in the straw nests.

'Step aside, mother, this omelet is my affair. To be just right,' he explained, breaking a tuft of broom over his knee, 'it must be cooked over a fire of broom. The flame browns the omelet better, and leaves it drooly inside; the smoke gives it just the taste it needs. Father, if you don't mind, will you take the plate, now, and stand in front of the door?'

The father took the plate and stood by the threshold.

The skillet stood on its tripod in the midst of the flame; the omelet sizzled. When he saw that it was ready, the cook tapped on the handle of the skillet. The omelet flew into the air, right up the chimney. Talking all the time, the cook went to the door, took the plate from his father's hand, and, without even looking up, held it out, and the omelet, nicely turned over, fell plop into it.

A lucky thing that the boy had taken the plate. The father, in his astonishment, would have let it fall.

Full of surprise and joy, the tears rolled into his moustache, big as white currants.

'Boys, boys, the house goes to all three of you! Who could choose between you?'

And who could?

And so the house remained their common property, and they lived there together. Between their trades there was no rivalry. Each one of the three could talk only of his brother's skill, and when his own name was mentioned, shrugged his shoulders. So their days were passed in perfect understanding; even their wives—oh miracle!—agreed. And as they lived on a footing of friendship, honour, and content, in spite of the envious, they lived until they died.

The Tale of the Sun
and the Moon

ONCE UPON A TIME, at Châteaugay, there were two vine-growers, Amable and Hippolyte, renowned among all vine-growers in those parts as the two greatest drinkers of them all. Which meant that when they really got going they really emptied the jugs.

One Sunday afternoon they met in the public square.

'Ha,' said Amable, after talking of this and that, 'my wife gave me peas and bacon to eat this noon, much too salty. I've had a raging thirst ever since.'

'Me too,' said Hippolyte. 'With me, it wasn't bacon, it was too long a nap. But it works the same way with me; the way I'm made, I sleep salty, and when I wake up I'm thirsty.'

'Well, let's have a drink,' they said together.

So they went into Amable's cellar; each of them took his silver wine-taster out of his pocket, and soon they were deep in discussion of vintage years and wines. When such a case comes before the jury, before they can reach a verdict, they must weigh the evidence very carefully.

They lingered there an hour or so, wandering from barrel to barrel.

When they left, and decided to go from this cellar to Hippolyte's, the whole place seemed to have been changed around.

The other cellar was only fifty feet away, straight ahead, where the village road led down to the plain. But the mayor and the councillors, with their crazy notions of politics, must have closed all the roads out of town. The houses were all turned around, so were the staircases and the cellars, and the road kept running into the walls.

They hunted about, from left to right, and finally found their way to the cellar. There they took their wine-tasters out of their pockets, and went on with the debate.

So long did they argue that it happened with them as it sometimes happens with the judges of Riom—they fell asleep over the evidence.

When they woke up and poked their noses out of doors, they felt chilly. Perhaps there was a bit of fog in the air, to confuse them. Still, anybody whose head was not going around could have seen well enough to find his way.

'What a moon!' said Amable, pointing up at it, round and bright over the roofs.

'Moon?' said Hippolyte, 'you must have been boozing. Can't you see it's the sun?'

'How can you have a pair of eyes in your head and speak such foolishness? I tell you it's the moon.'

'Moon yourself! it's the morning sun, I tell you. I'd know it by the thirst I've got; we've slept since yesterday evening.'

Morning or evening, moon or sun, the dispute went on.

'Hey,' said Amable suddenly, pointing to a man coming their way, 'there's someone who'll tell us! Tell us, fellow,

Hippolyte says that's the sun up there; I say it's the moon. Tell us who's right!'

'My poor friends,' said the man, who was also on his way home from a session in the cellars, 'I can't tell you that. . . . You see, I don't live here.'

The Tale of the Man who put up Such a Good Defence

ONCE UPON A TIME, in a certain village, there was an old bachelor who wanted a pot to melt grease in.

He might have gone to buy one in town, on the potters' street, but he was quite content to borrow one from his neighbour.

By ill luck, the cat tried to lick the pot, the man tried to chase the cat, the cat knocked over the pot, and you can imagine what happened.

But as luck would have it, the pot broke in two equal halves. The man joined the two pieces and brought the pot back to his neighbour, pressed together in his two hands; very carefully he placed it on the table, without a word of its breaking.

However, the neighbour had a sharp eye, and he saw it. He who breaks the eggs pays for the omelet. The same goes for pots. But the man would not hear a word of it. And so the neighbour went to law with him.

This time he had to go to town and consult a lawyer.

The lawyer asked him to explain all the ins and outs of the matter.

'And there were no witnesses when you borrowed it and brought it back?'

'No, sir, no witnesses.'

'In that case you can defend yourself in three ways. You can say that the pot, when it was lent you, was already broken. You can say that when you brought it back it was not broken—that it has been broken since then. Who can prove the contrary? Finally, you can say, and it would be simplest of all, that you never borrowed that pot from that neighbour. Yes, if you make a good defence, I don't see that you can be convicted, with no proof against you.'

'Very well, sir, and thank you, sir. I quite understand.'

'That will be a crown.'

It would have been cheaper to pay for the pot. But the man was so pleased to see what a fine defence he had—so easy, so unshakable!—that he handed over the crown with a good grace. He went back to his village, and waited there until he was called into court.

On the day for the hearing, as soon as his name was called, he got up, full of assurance, and went to the bar.

'Your Honour, for my defence, this is what I have to say. And just let him prove the contrary.'

'I am listening.'

'Firstly, it's like this: I claim that when it was loaned me, the pot was already broken. Secondly, it's like this: when I gave it back, the pot was in good condition. Thirdly and lastly, it's like this: I never, never borrowed any pot from my neighbour.'

He went back that evening to his village, as glum as he could be. And until the day of his death, he railed against the law and its servants, lawyers as well as judges.

The Tale of the Seven Brothers in the Well

ONCE UPON A TIME there were seven brothers of Auvergne, the hill country, who, at the beginning of the slack season, according to the custom of Auvergne, set out to earn their living in the world.

They were brothers, ah yes! all seven of them: not a one of them who did not have the six others for his brothers. That was always a big surprise to them when they thought of it, and it gave them a deal of self-confidence.

They weren't the sort of clever fellows who would ever invent gunpowder, but cleverness belongs to the devil. The eldest had promised his mother that by Saint John's Eve, Midsummer Eve, he would bring them all back home.

So there they were, out on the high-roads, wonder-struck at all they saw, and wanting to see everything close to—a chapel with its bell, a team of white horses, a high donkey-back bridge, a squirrel turning in his cage, everything, simply everything.

Towards evening they passed by a great well: you may be sure they had not seen many like it up in the hills, where the water flows in springs from the rocks.

They went near to admire it, and leaned over and looked at the water gleaming far below, until the eldest told them to be on their way.

But when they had gone three steps, the idea struck them that they had better count, to make sure that one of the seven had not fallen into the well.

The eldest lined them up and counted them. He only found six.

He went and stood in line, and told the youngest brother to fall out and count them in his turn.

The youngest brother too could only find six, so each of the others tried it, and each one only counted six, not one more.

'And, hang it! there were certainly seven of us!'

Yes, each one of these wise fellows forgot to count himself. They were in so much of a fret, you see, that it troubled their brains.

The eldest went back to the well and leaned over, squinting from beneath his hand. Was that not a face, now, down there at the bottom? And the others came to look, and thought the same thing.

No doubt about it. But they had no rope, no ladder, to pull their brother up.

'Well, we'll make a chain. I'll take hold of the railing: you, hang by my ankles, and so on for all of us!'

But six men of Auvergne make something of a weight. The seventh, climbing down from shoulder to shoulder, had hardly taken a grip of the one at the bottom, when the eldest, up at the top, a boy as strong as a horse, felt that his hands were losing their grip, and slipping from the rail.

'I'm slipping!' he cried.

And the youngest, misunderstanding, exclaimed, 'I'm spitting!'—spitting in his hands, he thought.

The Tale of the Seven Brothers in the Well

Good advice, and quickly followed. In no time at all there they were, all seven of them, at the bottom of the well.

Were they drowned? Oh no, not at all. There was just enough water for them to fall into, pell-mell, one on top of the other. What a jumble! They couldn't even manage to untangle themselves, to pull their legs and arms out of the heap—no one could tell which were his own.

So then the eldest had an idea—he usually had them for the crowd.

Since he was on top of the heap, he unbuckled his belt, and began to leather them with it, as hard as he could.

'Oh-yo-yo, my leg!'

'Oh-yo-yo, my hand!'

'Oh-yo-yo, my head!'

The belt was of good leather, half an inch thick, and it fell with a good round smack. Thanks to it, each one was able to recognize his own members, and could pull his arms or his ears out of the heap. The water, the ooze, and seven men of Auvergne—it all made a fine soup.

They extricated themselves, they stood up. At this moment the moon rose. They could see that there were gaps between the stones to climb out of the well by placing your feet in them and clinging with your hands.

Hole by hole, one after the other, they all climbed back, up to the meadow.

They shook themselves like wet dogs and shook the water out of their hats.

When they looked at these hats drying on the grass, the eldest got the idea of counting them, and he found that there were seven. So at last they knew that they were all there.

And off they went by the light of the moon, happier than ever to be seven brothers, and surer than ever that they would make their way anywhere in the world.

The Tale of the
Dangerous Post

ONCE UPON A TIME there was a woman, and a good woman she was, no doubt, as good as the rest of them and better than some, but not among the easiest to live with. Well, one day, for lack of the right medicine, perhaps, she up and died.

Her husband felt all the grief that was proper, that is sure—but, as they say, when your wife dies you wear a new hat.

They were carrying the deceased to her burial, when, as they were leaving the courtyard—the passage was narrow and slippery underfoot—one of the bearers made a false step, and the coffin bumped against the gatepost. It so happened that the deceased, who was not deceased, but fallen into a deep swoon, was awakened by the shock, and she groaned.

They all fell to shouting and running about, and finally they opened the coffin.

She heaved a sigh. . . . Instead of carrying her to her grave, they carried her back to her bed, and she went on living.

Several years later the woman who was not dead died again.

It seemed to be for good this time. The doctor was called in, and certified that she was dead.

But on the day of the funeral, when the bearers were about to leave the courtyard, the poor widower went two steps ahead of them and stood against the gate.

'Look out there, all of you! For God's sake, now, watch out for that post!'

The Tale of the Well-Salted Soup

ONCE UPON A TIME there was a large farm, down over there at the end of the road, where there lived father, mother, son, and daughter.

The boy, who had come of age, had married and brought his wife home.

It is well said, 'In a house there should be only one woman and one oven.' These three petticoats did not have the same ways of doing things; mother and daughter kept to one side, daughter-in-law to the other. And the house went all ways at once.

One day it happened that the tailor came there for a day's work; on such occasions they take more trouble than usual over the dinner.

Mother gave her orders to daughter-in-law, and ended up with, 'And above all, don't forget to salt the soup!'

This was her way of reminding daughter-in-law that she had forgotten to do so two nights ago.

After which, wrinkling up her nose, mother went off to give the hens their grain.

Well and good. A moment later, daughter came back from tending the sheep.

'I must be sure and salt the soup,' she said to herself. 'Sister-in-law is so careless that she will forget to do it, as she did day before yesterday.'

She came into the house, took a handful of salt out of the wooden sabot nailed up by the fireplace—that's what they use for a salt-box in our country—and threw the salt in the kettle. Then, well pleased with herself, she went back to her sheep.

Soon mother reappeared.

'I must be sure and salt the soup. Sure and certain, feather-brains would forget it.'

So she threw in her handful of salt, and went to take the cows out.

Daughter-in-law came in.

'I'd best not forget to salt the soup, since the old woman reminded me of it. If I had the bad luck to forget it, I'd never hear the end of it.'

She too threw her handful of salt in the kettle and left.

The tailor, as he sat cross-legged on the table cutting his cloth, watched the women over his spectacles. He was hunch-backed, and malicious like all hunchbacks. He had not said a word to warn the second woman, nor even the third; the soup would be uneatable. But that was just it: he had seen that there was better to eat than soup—smoked ham and sausages, hanging from the rafters. He rose in his turn, went to the sabot, took a fistful of salt, and two more besides, and threw them all into the kettle.

At noon, daughter-in-law put the soup on the table, and put slices of bread to soak in it. Father came back, and they sat down at table. Father was first to taste the soup. Quietly he set down his spoon.

'You must have forgotten to salt it.'

Immediately the three women fell to protesting.

'I salted it, and I put in as much as usual!'

'I salted it! I'm sure I put in my handful!'

'I salted it! Yes, I salted it, for fear it would be forgotten again!'

'Good,' said father, 'if all of you put in the needful, that's why it puckers up your mouth. Wife, give us the ham: it will be less salty than the soup. And you, daughter, make a salad.'

Father had a sharp eye, and it did not escape him that the hunchback was well pleased to be eating something better.

'But you, now—you were right here in the room: you saw them come in, one after the other. Couldn't you warn them that the soup was already salted?'

'Ah! *ma foi!* I thought that was the custom of the house. Everybody here must salt the soup, I thought. So, of course, I wanted to do like the others, and I too put in my handful of salt!'

The Tale of the Little Frog

ONCE UPON A TIME, at Saint-Amand-Roche-Savine, there was a king who had three sons. Now this king was getting on in years: a bit stiff-jointed, a bit deaf; in short, he felt tired, and he would gladly have disposed of his kingdom before a notary.

But to whom should he give his crown? Old he might be, but he had not yet lost his wits. 'My three boys,' he had to admit, 'can't be called the cleverest of the clever.'

Well, no, they would never have set the river on fire. Especially the youngest, the one they called Bedoce. Poor Bedoce! Half-witted? By no means, but inclined to be simple and innocent, guileless of heart and short of wit.

The king thought of his three sons, and sighed.

One fine day, since he knew he must, he decided to try them out.

'Stupid they are, stupid they will remain. Who could change their skins? If only they could marry some girl with plenty of wit, that would make up for their lack of it. It's the wife who makes the home.'

In those days women were spinners first of all. One morning at breakfast the royal father called his sons, gave them each one a plant of hemp, and charged them to see that it was hackled and spun into thread.

'We shall see which of the three of you brings me the finest ball of thread, well-twisted, smooth, even, strong! In a word, the best spun. I may tell you that I shall consider it a matter of the highest importance.'

As stupid as they were, they understood that the crown would go to the winner. At least, the two eldest understood so.

They left for Fournols, where they went to the pasture-grounds. In those days all the shepherdesses kept their flocks there. It was then the Cross of May—the third of May, the day when they let out the cows at winter's end. They were all skirmishing about in the tender green grass, cutting capers and switching their tails.

And the shepherdesses ran after their cows, shouting, laughing, and having a merry time. The mountain was alive with them. The two eldest sons went to help the girls; they slapped the cows about, shouted, and had a merry time too. At last they found what they were after. Each of the boys chose a girl for himself, in all good faith and troth, a fine figure of a girl, buxom, bouncing, with cheeks red as an apple.

When each one had chosen his intended, he gave her his hemp, and told her what was wanted. Straight away, full of good-will, the girls set about their spinning. Perhaps they were not too skilful—with their great hands like washing-paddles they twisted the thread as thick as their little fingers —but they did what they could, with all their hearts. The two eldest sons, each with a blade of grass in his mouth and his nose in the air, went back as proud as peacocks to their father's castle.

During this time, what was Bedoce doing?

Ah, yes, Bedoce! He had started to follow his brothers to

the pasture, but he followed them at a distance, like a beaten dog, for he thought that even the most bereft of the shepherdesses would have none of him.

His brothers looked back, and when they saw his hang-dog air, they told each other that Bedoce would disgrace them. They called him a simpleton and chased him away, waving their arms.

'The girls would go for you with their staffs, you poor dunce!'

Carrying his hemp like a candle, Bedoce took refuge beyond the meadow in the wood of the Fays. Once there, he sank down on a stone and began to weep. As large as peas, the tears rolled from his eyes to his chin and fell in the brook.

Sorrow had such a hold on him that he did not even see a little green frog hop out of the water upon his sabot, and look up at him with compassion. By God's leave, the frog began to talk.

'How now! how now! how now! What's the matter? Tell me, poor Bedoce!'

Bedoce was such an innocent that he was not unduly surprised to hear a green frog call him by his name. He lifted his nose again, still holding his hemp like a candle.

'What's the matter with me? Tell you, poor frog? Well, it's this way: my father's growing old, and wants to dispose of the kingdom, and he has given each of us a bunch of hemp to be spun. The crown, my brothers say, will go to the one who brings back the finest and prettiest thread. They've gone to court the shepherdesses and pick out a sweetheart among them. But I have no sweetheart to look kindly on me; no girl will spin my hemp.'

'Now, now, now! Give it to me, your tow, and I'll spin it for you, now, yes, now!'

'You! Ho, you're only a frog! How could you spin? Or twist your thread?'

'How, how, how? Give it to me! Give it to me! In eight days, come again, and call to me!

> Froggy green, froggy wee,
> Froggy-love, come to me!

Then you'll see, poor Bedoce, then you'll see!'

'Well, here then, what can I lose? Take the hemp, poor frog!'

No sooner did the frog have the tow than she hopped back with it into the brook.

And Bedoce, nose drooping toward his sabots, asking himself if he had not been dreaming, went back to his father.

One morning at breakfast-time the king called to his boys.

'The week is over; the hemp should be spun. Let each of you bring me his ball of thread.'

The two eldest went gaily off to the pasture.

And Bedoce, what could he do? With his tow at the bottom of the brook, in the care of a frog! But to do as his brothers did, for lack of something better, he went to the wood of the Fays.

He came to the edge of the brook, and how green was the grass! 'My frog was greener yet,' he said to himself. And indeed it was green: there were drops of water everywhere, on the tips of the grass-blades, in the clefts of the leaves. And it was full of flowers—forget-me-nots, pansies, speedwell, cowslips, buttercups, and mignonette. Flowers everywhere! an abundance of greenery, colours, youth, and innocent freshness—touches of blue, red and rose, violet, scarlet, flashing in the sunlight.

All the multitudinous life of the meadow, like the multitudinous carols of the larks in the middle of the air, and the thousand voices of the river, flowing over its bright stones. It opened up to Bedoce's mind a marvellous land of verdure and pearly waters, in which his little green frog was queen. Bemused as by an enchantment, he could not so

much as remember the words he should use to call his little friend.

'Froggy frog, greeny frog. . . .'

'How now, how now, how now?' said the frog, hopping from the brook as green and dainty as the grass and the flowers. 'Couldn't you, for love of me, say it properly?

> Froggy green, froggy wee,
> Froggy-love, come to me!

Come on, try it!'

He said it over, poor Bedoce, and his friend the frog then gave him a spindle of thread. And what thread! strong as brass wire, but even finer than a cobweb.

'Oh, thank you, my frog, thank you for all your trouble!'

'You see, you see! Poor Bedoce, this you'll bring to your royal sire the king. Merrily, for love of me!'

Joyfully he thanked his frog sweetheart, and his eyes, candid and friendly, spoke his thanks even better. Then he put the spindle in the pocket of his smock and went back to his father's castle.

The two elder brothers had just arrived, and both of them had presented their balls of thread. The king shook his head and sighed, for their thread was as heavy as clothes-line, full of knots and splinters.

At that moment his youngest made his appearance. The king raised his eyes and signed to him to approach. From this son, poor Bedoce, he expected almost nothing. However, to satisfy his conscience, he asked for the boy's thread.

Bedoce took the spindle from his pocket and offered it respectfully upon his hat. The king took it, looked at it, looked closer, and nearly fell off his throne.

'No, really,' he said under his breath. 'No, but really, now!'

He was too surprised to say more. He was hardly expecting this! A thread that might have been spun by the queen of spinners—even, smooth, fine as silk: the king pulled hard but couldn't break it—wound and unwound it, never tired of admiring it.

'Still and all, I can't give the kingdom into the hands of a poor innocent. And then, it's not enough for a woman to be a good spinner. She must, she must . . .'

At that moment, as luck would have it, the prime minister came to tell the king that his dog had just given birth to three pretty little pups.

'Good,' said the king, 'that's just what we needed. My sons, here are three lap-dogs to bring up: take one, each of you. He who in three months shall bring me back the best-trained dog shall have my kingdom.'

The two eldest sons thrust their puppies, blind and whimpering, into their blouses. The next day, back they went to Fournols and the pasture, where they gave the nurslings to their shepherdesses.

As for Bedoce, he went back to his brook, more woe-begone than the first time. His tears fell like spring rain down to his breast-bone.

'How now, how now, how now?' croaked the Little Frog, hopping on to the turf. 'The thread wouldn't do? Tell me true!'

'Indeed yes, poor frog, your thread was by far the finest; it might have been spun by a queen's hand. But now our father has given us each a little dog—yes, a dog for our sweethearts to raise. And I have no lady: what shall I do? Look at him, poor little ball of a puppy!'

'Give him to me, give him to me! Am I not your fair lady?'

'Oh, but you would drown him, my Little Frog!'

'That I won't, that I won't! Give him to me; after months one two three, come again and you will see. But this time, remember the rhyme:

>Froggy green, froggy wee,
>Froggy-love, come to me!

That's how it goes—see? So now, trust to me!'

Amazed and enchanted, poor Bedoce repeated it after her, and Little Frog, carrying the new-born puppy, plunged down into the depths of the water, among the weeds.

Bedoce was not only touched by her kindness, he was transformed by it. He still could make nothing of it all, but from the bottom of his heart he trusted in his Little Frog.

Back he went to his father's castle, walking on air. And the three months, May, June, July, passed by as though under the spell of a dream.

The day came when the king asked for the little dogs. The two elder sons ran to Fournols, and their shepherdesses gave them their dogs. As dogs, they couldn't be called beauties. Hair all tousled, full of burrs and filth, like the ball of thread, and about the same smutty colour. And they lifted their legs against all the tables and coffers. They weren't even good for driving the cows to pasture! All they knew how to do was to frisk about, slobber, chew up shoes, and bark until they split your ears.

Bedoce had gone to the wood of the Fays, and this time, when he came to the brook, he knew what he should say:

'Froggy green, froggy wee,
Froggy-love, come to me!'

'At last you've come, at last you've come!' cried Little Frog at once, hopping into the meadow. 'Here's the thing you may bring to show the king!'

At the same time she showed him, asleep in a basket with a pink ribbon around his neck, a little lap-dog, white as snow and soft as silk, washed, combed, and curled, smelling of honeysuckle.

Bedoce did his best to thank his Little Frog, but his words fell short of what was in his heart. And he was so proud to show off this little dog, so well trained, that in a quarter of an hour he was back at his father's castle.

No sooner had he set down his basket in the great hall

than the little dog jumped out, ran to the king, presented his paw, and gave him back caress for caress. He showed a hundred pretty tricks, wagging his tail, but hardly ever yapping. Then, as, for his own reasons, he wanted to go out, he went to the door and discreetly scratched at it.

During this time the elder brothers' dogs barked, dashed about, chewed up the king's slippers, and—if you will excuse me—left puddles everywhere.

The king, very much embarrassed, shook his head.

'Well,' he concluded, 'a woman isn't perfect because she is clever at spinning or knows how to raise dogs. She must know how to manage a household, and how to bear herself in any company.'

'My sons,' he said, 'listen: now you are to bring me your ladies. He who has chosen the best and the fairest shall have the crown.'

The elder brothers took to their heels and climbed up to Fournols at top speed. Since their eyes were none of the sharpest, nor their wits of the nimblest, they had seen little difference between the three balls of thread, nor even between the three dogs. And, as each of them was proud of his girl and thought her the most beautiful girl in the world, he was quite sure in his own mind of winning.

There are such nice shepherdesses, up on the mountain! And they had chosen those with the reddest face and the brightest clothes, and so round that you could roll them from top to bottom of the meadow. As if they only wanted them by the pound! Well, they got what they wanted. These were real bouncers. Even their clothes were solid, made of wool—as thick as your hand, and able to stand alone, like bells.

Well, then, that was their choice. Everyone to his taste: a girl's only fair if you find her so!

And Bedoce?

Poor Bedoce, very much shaken, had gone to the wood of

the Fays. More out of habit than in hope. The tears rolled down from his eyes to his sabots. He had called Little Frog, and he had told her his troubles. This time the game was up; no longer was it a matter of a ball of thread, a little dog. . . .

'My father wants us to bring him our ladies. So now, Little Frog, what am I to do? No lady fair have I!'

'How now, how now, how now? Oh Bedoce, I'm here!'

'You, my Little Frog? You are the green frog of the grasses and the running water! Can you see me bringing a frog, and saying that she is to be my wife?'

'Trust in me, trust in me! Your wife I'll be, and you shall see!'

'Ah, poor Little Frog, what would I do with you? Let you leap from stone to stone on the floor of my father's castle?'

'First, come home with me and you shall see. Trust in me, Bedoce, trust in me. Your wife I'll be.'

'I'm willing. My wife, so be it.'

Ah, from the bottom of his heart, he trusted his Little Frog. She drew him to the brook; well he might have feared to drown, but he trusted in her, in the running water, the speedwell, and forget-me-not. He threw himself into the water with his sweetheart.

No sooner were they down in the water than it drew away, and before them appeared a most beautiful castle, a castle of mirrors and silver, such as no one could have believed there was in the world. Oh, such a wonder! And that was nothing beside another marvel: beside the boy there was no longer a green frog, but a beautiful princess, all in the colours of hope, the fairest of the fair! By a spell cast on her, as often happened in those days, when she was a king's daughter she had been changed into a frog in the grass. A fairy spell which could only be broken when a king's son should agree to make her his wife under the form of a frog.

What was needed was a lamb like Bedoce, one of those innocents who can see clearer than the others. One of those who love simple things in a simple way—fresh water, green grass with pearls of dew, all under the greenwood tree, tirra lee.

And Bedoce the king's son found as a sweetheart and his life's companion this little green princess with her heart as pure as a pearl! No sooner had he seen her as a princess than he felt his mind open and stretch, and, when he had taken her hand, he was stupid no longer.

A coach was waiting for them at the door, all of mirrors set in silver. But they had no need of mirrors: each one's eyes served as mirror for the other. They stepped into the coach, her hand in his. He, candid as a child, laughing and bold, wide-awake and wondering: she, his sweetheart, Little Frog, fine and dainty as was never a girl on earth, wiser than any other, and yet as bemused as he. All ready—off, coachman!

They came to the king's castle, followed by a throng of people who had recognized Bedoce—he was beloved throughout the countryside. One called to another, they all came running after, and in honour of the radiant pair they threw their caps in the air and wore their broadest grins.

At the castle the two bouncing shepherdesses were already installed—two stout half-giantesses, with faces as broad as barrels and red as holly-berries. Each one was wondering which would give orders to the other; indeed, they had begun to look askance at one another.

But, at the jingling of coach bells and the joyful cries of the people, all the court came tumbling out of the door, in a great commotion. Ha, what did they see? Bedoce, yes, it was Bedoce, the same and yet not the same; he leaped to the ground, alert as a sparrow, offered his hand to the prettiest of princesses, and, barely touching it, she stepped lightly down. Bedoce's hat in his hand, they both came to bow low before the king.

'Father, here is my sweetheart!'

'My son,' the king came near saying, 'here is my crown!'

But he was a prudent king. 'It's not enough,' he said to himself, 'for a girl to be a fine spinner, or clever at training animals, or fair of face and graceful in bearing; you must see her in her house to know what she's good for.'

Just then, as if fate meant to put to the test the three daughters-in-law to be, the king fell sick.

Not sick just to try them out. The surprise had given him a turn, in good earnest. Sick, really sick. 'At least I'll be well cared for, with three daughters-in-law around me!'

But the brides of the two elder sons had only one accomplishment: to look more blooming every day, so well did the cooking in the castle—roasts, patties, and pies—agree with them. They did only that: thrive, and nothing else, for you cannot do but one thing well at a time. But Little Frog knew how to care for the father of her betrothed, how to prepare for him herb tea sweetened with honey, or some dainty hot from the oven: how to amuse him when he wanted it, and let him rest when he needed it.

So well did she nurse him that in three days he was on his feet again. And the first thing the king did, when he could put his shoes on, was to give his kingdom to Bedoce, for love of the Little Frog.

'To the wedding! Good people, come to the wedding!'

Yes, all Saint-Amand was there. And they married off the elder sons at the same time, giving them plenty of land, woods and castles, so that their good shepherdesses could always enjoy taking the cows to pasture. In this way everybody was so happy that they were all kings and queens.

> Here's some cakes I brought from the ball.
> Deary me! I've eaten them all.

The Tale of the Miser who was Robbed

ONCE UPON A TIME there was a miser, rich by the hundreds and thousands. But he ate only barley bread—so that he might eat white bread, no doubt, in his coffin; he drank only cold water, and not too much of that, and slept on two fingers' thickness of straw under a ragged coverlet; and he kept no fire going: he warmed himself by the smoke when his cows dropped their dung. He scrimped, scrimped, scrimped. His one passion was to cut a halfpenny off his expenses, or else to make a penny profit somewhere else. And so he went his way through life, poking his nose ahead like a woman who is for ever feeling her hens' behinds to see if they are going to lay an egg.

And when he had raked in all he could, he turned that all into golden louis. All these louis he put into a large pot for salt pork, and he buried the pot under the belly of a stone. That was his secret place, at the foot of the garden, between

31

the curbstone of a well and the box hedge.

He never suspected that for many a long day a certain man had been climbing up the church tower to spy on him.

One evening he went out in the moonlight, raised the stone, and found no pot.

A fine state the miser was in—bellowing, groaning, tearing his hair.

Underneath the pale moon, he ran to see his goddaughter, his niece and sole heir, who lived at the other end of the town.

And there, how he complained, how he bawled, how he pranced!

'I'm robbed, I've lost my all! Nothing left for me but to hang myself!'

At last she understood what had happened. She was a good girl, even-tempered, cheerful, and quick-witted. Let us be ready, she thought, for whatever comes! But she knew that she couldn't preach a sermon to her godfather.

'Listen, godfather,' she said, however, 'don't be cast down.'

'What, you think that's possible? When such a calamity has befallen me—when I know that I've lost my all, everything. . . .'

'Lost everything? How do you know? If you should promise me not to ask the thief's name, nor any other questions, and if I should put the pot back in its hiding-place, perhaps it would turn out that you hadn't lost anything, after all.'

'What's that, girl? What are you saying?'

'Well, godfather, suppose that your thief, overcome with remorse, has come to bring me back the pot, making me swear to keep it quiet . . .'

'Yes . . .'

'And that I have promised, for my part, that I will put it back under the stone, and for yours, that you'll make no inquiries. You won't look about, you won't even take any steps.'

'But the pot! I want to see my pot, so I may count my gold!'

'Listen, godfather. If you leave it all to me, you have lost nothing. The pot is under the stone, and you are not to touch it; just go on as usual.'

'But I want to see my yellow boys; I must see them and touch them.'

'Just think a little: as long as you spend just the same as before, you are just as rich as before.'

'Ha, poor silly creature! How dare you? Ha, is that what you're about? Ha, I see now how the song goes!'

'Godfather, do listen: you drank cold water: well, go on drinking it; you ate barley bread, go on eating it; you slept upon straw, keep on sleeping on straw, and heating yourself at the smoke of the cow-dung. You will live the same life. All that you thought you had yesterday, just go on thinking that you have it. And, when you look at it that way, what have you lost, after all?'

'Ha, crazy woman, ha, poor silly creature! Hey, I've lost my gold pieces, and you can find only idle songs like that to sing me!'

Tearing out his hair by handfuls, he went home again, shut himself in, went down to the garden, and hanged himself from the great pear-tree, under the rays of the moon.

But, since through sheer avarice he had chosen his oldest rope, the rope broke.

He fell to earth and broke his two legs.

They heard his cries and came to find him. And the end of it was that, with his broken legs, he had to go back to his old life—drinking water, eating barley bread, sleeping on straw and warming himself at you know what—in short, whatever he had done before, spending the same niggardly bit. The niece was right: whether or no there was a pot of gold under the stone's belly made very little difference. But was he ever easy in mind about it, as she was? Did he come to say at last that he was still as rich as ever?

33

The Tale of Sainte Madeleine

ONCE UPON A TIME there was a saint, and her name was Madeleine. But the tale begins in the days before she was a saint.

It was on the morning of Candlemas, and the Virgin was on her way to mass. There in the orchard she saw Madeleine, displaying her charms, dallying with three fair youths.

'Madeleine, Madeleine, come with me to mass.'

'Why are there no young men with you, Holy Virgin? Gladly then would I go with you. But there is no fair youth in your company to be my companion!'

'There you are wrong, Madeleine. We have the fairest youth of them all.'

'Wait for me, Holy Virgin, while I put on my finery.'

She called her mother to comb her with a comb of pure silver, and she let down her hair, which fell in a flood of gold to her heels. Then she put on her crown, and you would have said that the sun was shining. And she put on her robe

34

of seven yards of brocade, whose train lay on the grass behind her; then her apron of silk in more than all the colours of the rainbow. And she girt herself with her golden girdle, that went forty times around her middle.

So resplendent was she that, as she passed along the road, all the trees burst into flower: when she crossed the church-yard, all the bells began to ring: when she entered the church, all the candles lit of themselves.

But when she stretched out her hand for the holy water, the font moved away along the wall.

And when she bent her knee, all the altars trembled and shook.

Nay, even the priest could no longer say the mass, the altar-boy could no longer give the responses.

'Go on, priest, say the mass, and boy, make your responses.'

'Softly, softly, Madeleine—humble your pride.'

'I shall humble it for no man, nor humble it for you. The good God himself gave it to me; I shall wear it every day.'

But when Our Lord said, 'O Madeleine, sinner before God, why have you sinned so greatly?' she could but tremble, bow her head, and say very low, 'Lord my God, there is no sin I find in myself.'

'Madeleine, Madeleine, sinner before God, go, hide yourself for seven years in the mountains.'

Seven years she abode in the mountains. The cave where she lived was higher up than the wood of tall pine trees, higher than the grey rocks, higher than the cloud in the path of the lightning.

At the end of seven years she made her way down between the rocks, and knelt beside the stream. Beside the wild-rose bushes she bathed her white hands in the softly flowing water. Then she held them up to the sun, and admired them.

'Madeleine, Madeleine, sinner before God, go you back and stay there seven more years!'

'Lord my God, I have well deserved the penance, and I will stay there as long as You wish.'

And back she went to live in the cave that was higher than the pines, the rocks, the clouds. She lived there on roots and cold water, wrapped up in her hair as in a shepherd's mantle.

At the end of seven years, when dawn fell on the dewy grass, Our Lord came to her.

'And now, Madeleine, holy saint of God, go you into Paradise.'

The Tale of the Dead Man who was Warm

ONCE UPON A TIME, in a certain town, there was a doctor who had a lot of learning at his finger-tips. So much so that it led to stories being whispered about him. They might as well have accused him of being a sorcerer; what they said was that he had been known to buy corpses and to cut them up. And so he had, for he was eager to understand the workings of our poor human body. But some respect should be shown the dead, however strong may be your love of medicine.

One fine spring day, some rich folk up in the hills had sent for him. That they were rich you may be sure—otherwise, in those bygone days, people who were about to die didn't usually send for a doctor; as they said, they could die without his help.

The doctor saw to his patient; he cured him—at least, he told him what he should do to be cured, if God were willing.

As he was about to leave, climbing into his wicker dog-cart with his man, the maid-servant ran after him. 'Oh, doctor, here's a young man from the village who knew that you were here. He's come to ask you to see his father, who's very bad.'

The father had just been struck by a fit of apoplexy. There was nothing he hadn't done, that fellow, especially when it came to guzzling and drinking. After which he'd go home drunk enough to fight with the walls, cursing, swearing, hitting out, carrying on. His poor wife had died of blows and of sorrow.

The maid-servant told all this, under her breath, and, to end with, 'Yes, doctor, now it must be his turn, and you can't save him from going through with it, nor from what must be waiting for him in the other world. "Your bed's made in hell, and there you shall lie!"—that's what his poor wife used to say to him every evening, and what she said, everyone else thought. In these parts they never called that fellow anything but Bedamned!'

She would have kept on, but the doctor shrugged his shoulders. 'In hell, in hell, it will be up to him to save his own skin. We'll try to save it in this world. Send me the young man!'

The young man came, and the doctor questioned him briefly; he made him get into the carriage between his servant and himself, and guide them to his father's house.

When they arrived, the man was at the last gasp. He showed only the whites of his eyes, like a sick bird. The doctor opened a vein in his arm and tried to bleed him, but no blood came. He applied other remedies, he did his best. But when the hour comes, it comes, and all the learned men of the world can do nothing. The man's throat rattled three times, and he died.

'Doctor,' said the young man, as the doctor was putting on his coat, 'if you'll tell me how much I should give you?

. . . We lived very poorly, my father and I, and there's not much money in the house.'

The doctor stopped a minute, like a man who has just had an idea.

'What if I made you an offer? I'll be the one to give you something—five or six crowns, if you like. . . . But we'll keep this quiet. It's all for a good end. I'm in need of a body for my medical studies.'

'After all,' the young man said to himself, 'who'd know about it? I'll put a log with straw stuffed about it in the coffin. If there's any who come to sprinkle holy water on it, they'll find the coffin nailed up.'

'Doctor,' he said at last, 'that is worth ten crowns.'

'All right, let it be ten crowns.'

Dusk was falling, and the house was in an out-of-the-way spot. The doctor and his servant each took the dead man by one arm, and the son wrapped round him an old moth-eaten greatcoat, and pulled down over his head a fur cap. The two men set him between them on the seat of the cart, and off they went.

It was dark: the north wind was blowing, and it was cold, out there on the mountain roads. The horse climbed slowly uphill toward the pass, where there was an old inn. As the minutes went by, doctor and man felt the dead man grow as stiff as an iron bar and cold as an icicle.

'Master,' said the man, 'I don't know if you feel the same way, but this comrade we've got here, this so-called Be-damned, is freezing me down to the very spine. What do you say to a shot of hot wine at the inn?'

'I'd say it was a good idea. Here we are—stop right now.'

They got down, and ordered wine, steaming hot.

While they were inside, the innkeeper came back from the woods, with his son-in-law, one jovial fellow with another. They recognized the doctor's dog-cart and through the window they could see him in the brightly lit room, drinking hot wine.

'What godless men they are, to leave this poor man outside here! Leave him like a dog, a dumb beast, in this bitter weather, while they sit over a bowl of hot wine you can smell from here. . . .'

They went up to the dog-cart. By his fur cap and greatcoat, the innkeeper recognized the man, the rascal they called Bedamned. But why was he here? They had been told along the road that he had just died. . . . In these small places each bit of news travels fast, and in less than a quarter of an hour it had spread from one end of the village to the other.

'It's him all right, dead as a door-nail, just like they told me—frozen stiff. What on earth can be going on?'

The innkeeper was a quick-witted man. He knew what was said about the doctor, and it didn't take him long to understand. Always ready for a prank, he had an idea. He scratched his head, and then, 'Come here,' he said to his son-in-law 'Help me.'

In a moment the doctor and his man came back. They climbed hastily up on the seat—it was bitter cold—sat down on each side of the man in fur cap and greatcoat, and, shaking the reins, the man clucked to the horse.

At first they did not speak. A dead man is not as enlivening a companion as you might wish for.

'It will be a cold night,' the doctor said at last. 'Luckily the wine has warmed me up.'

'Master,' said the man, 'do you know what? The dead man has warmed up too. Since I had that wine he's felt quite warm to me.'

'Confound it, I'd say the same. But we're dreaming. I certified him dead, for good and all.'

'Listen, certified or not, I swear to you that dead man is warm.'

And at that, all of a sudden:

The Tale of the Dead Man who was Warm

'Warm?' said the dead man, in a flat, contemptuous voice, 'warm? down where I am, you may well say it's burning!'

Powers of God! think of it! The servant threw the reins to one side, the doctor threw his case to another, and off they scampered across the countryside as if the dead man and all hell with him were at their heels.

If they had only looked back, they would have seen the horse turn about, and the dead man, still on the seat of the dog-cart, set off back toward his house.

However, he went no farther than the inn. There he got down, took off the cap and greatcoat, and returned them to the real dead man, who was waiting patiently, sitting on a wheelbarrow in the toolshed. Then he took up the shafts of the wheelbarrow, and in five minutes the false dead man, that is, the innkeeper, had trundled the true dead man back home. He knocked at the door until the young man came.

'Here, I've come back with your father. Put him straight in his coffin, and tomorrow we'll give him a Christian burial. . . . But what came over you? Now he's dead, do you think you should let him go gallivanting about like this?'

The Tale of the Land of Long Nights

ONCE UPON A TIME there were two tinkers, perhaps a bit thick-headed but good enough fellows for all that. And both of them just alike. Except that one of them liked his platter of stew, the other his jug of wine. But each one was very careful of his pennies, and never wanted to take them out of his purse once he had put them in.

For this reason they usually slept at farms, in the hay-mows, so that they were not obliged to spend two pennies at the inn—in those days, that was the price of a night's lodging. Such economy! But they were none the worse for it.

It happened once, in a part of the country where there were no farms, only villages, that they were overtaken by nightfall. They walked until they were ready to drop. They slept as they walked, they walked as they slept; their eyes kept shutting, and they moved as if they were machines. And not a house all along the road . . . not a barn. At last they reached a town. They hung back a bit, but there they were, with a cold wind blowing, the one they call poor Jeanne, that nips you and makes you shiver; they couldn't very well lie down on the cobbles of the market-place and pick up a few straws for a blanket, so they went to the inn.

'Ha!' said their host, 'a place to sleep? The fact is, to-morrow's fair day; it's a big fair, all kinds of merchants, and I've a houseful of them to look after—I don't see anywhere to put you.'

'Oh,' said one of the tinkers, nearly asleep on his feet, 'as long as we have room to stretch out, we're not fussy.'

'Oh, yes,' said the other, wobbling about like a drunken man, 'a bit of straw in a corner and I'll sleep as tight as a tick.'

'Well, then,' said the host, 'come along.'

He took them upstairs, down to the end of a corridor, and then through a large room, into a cubby-hole where no day-light could get in. A closet with no other window than a panel in the back of a wall-cupboard, opening on to the hall. The kitchen-boy had once slept there.

The tinkers were fellows who blew their noses on their sleeves, and they did not worry about the niceties. They barely glanced at their makeshift room; all they wanted was sleep.

'This will do; we'll sleep here as soon as anywhere, and we'll get up as early.'

Out of habit, just as they did at a farmhouse, they handed over their matches and knives to their host.

Again out of habit, that of seizing any chance of cutting expenses, 'Only, see here: for this room, we'll only pay a penny for the night.'

'A penny, so be it,' said the innkeeper, taking the matches. 'And for a penny I'll let you make as long a night of it as in the rooms of the quality. Till tomorrow, then!'

He left, taking the candle, leaving them to sleep without any light as though they were in a barn. Because he had just thought of a good trick. He shut the door after him, and at the same moment he was careful to drop the candlestick; under cover of the clatter, he turned the key in the lock without their hearing him. So there, a good long night to you!

He went downstairs, and winked at the merchants drinking below. 'We'll have a good game if we hold on!' And in a few words he explained the matter.

The two tinkers, who had toiled all day, packs on their backs, looking for work from house to house or doing their jobs in the village squares—the two tinkers undressed, lay down, and slept like lumps of lead.

They slept so hard that they were still at it next morning. But at last they did awake. Each one opened an eye. Darkness, nothing but darkness. Afraid of waking his comrade before daylight, neither one moved at first—they hardly dared roll over. But one was hungry, the other thirsty, and they felt emptier by the minute. They fell to dreaming, one of a great smoking dish of stew, so thick the spoon stood upright in it, and the other of cool red wine, tumblers and bumpers full, with the bottle on the table.

'You might think the night was over,' mumbled the one, 'by the thirst that's on me.'

'It can't be so,' mumbled the other. 'I'm too hungry tonight; it's as though day were here already.'

They sighed, stretched, and sighed again.

'Asleep?'

'And you?'

'I've slept my fill—I'd like some stew.'

'For myself, I'd like a drink.'

'But you see, it's not yet daylight.'

'All the same . . .'

They listened hard. In their ear-tight closet, up at the back of the inn, the few sounds that came to them, voices and mooings, footsteps and rolling wheels, were like the muffled roar of the wind in the tree-tops. They waited, they listened, while time went by. They began to yawn—so loud you could hear them from the fair grounds—'Ah-ha-ha-ha! Ah-ha-ha-ha!' They stretched their arms, wriggled their shoulders, and yawned and yawned.

One of them could stand it no more. He got up, in his shirt-tails, felt his way in the dark, found the bolt of the cupboard door, opened it, and poked his nose at what he thought was the window, sniffing the air and looking for daylight.

No more daylight than in the inside of an oven.

So he went back to his pallet and lay down. 'Sometimes it's like that: you think the night's over and it's not.' They tried to nap again, they tossed and turned. But sleep would not come: what did come, grumbling louder, was hunger for the stew man, thirst for the bottle man.

Somewhere in the house they heard a clock strike twelve. Midnight or midday? They both got up, went to the door, and found it locked. So they fell to hammering on it, bellowing and calling for the host.

He came running in his underpants and nightcap, candle in hand.

'What's the matter with you there? Only just struck midnight, and you wake us up? . . . Go back to bed, be quiet! or else my guests will come to teach you a lesson. That's enough carrying-on. Back to bed, and wait for morning.'

As though he were angry, he slammed the door on them, and turned the key once more.

Ruefully they went back to their pallet. With all their might, they tried to sleep again. But one could see only a smoking dish of stew, thick with cabbage, tender potatoes, and slices of brown bread—the other, brimming glasses and bottles in a row.

So beautiful was the dream that at last they fell asleep. Late in the afternoon, noses buried in the straw, they both snored hard enough to shake the inn.

The story of the two tinkers asleep at the inn had been all over the fair since that morning. People came to the Golden Lion as they would go to a play, and asked about the two sleepers. Some of them even went up the staircase on tiptoe and listened at the cupboard door to the snoring that rumbled like a millwheel. The tinkers slept, slept, slept. . . .

But they had to wake at last, and this time they were so hungry and thirsty that they could hardly bear it. Would the night never end, the door never open?

They tried to be patient, at least until they heard a clock strike. But, to help on the joke, the host had stopped the clock.

At last the bottle man thought he was losing his mind. He sprang at the door, scratched it, shook it.

'Come on, lie down! Do you want to wake everybody up again?'

'Look, I'll wake them very softly. . . .'

At first he went at it softly, but then they both lost patience. Once more there were blows and bellowings.

The host came running, again in his underpants, leaving the door open so that those below could hear.

'Are you crazy, you two? Or sick? . . . What, eat and drink? What's ailing you? Everyone wants to sleep. So much the worse for you!'

The tipplers below had followed, and were listening from the staircase—merchants, servants, and neighbours, struggling to keep back their laughter. Shoulders shook, tears streamed from their eyes—the inn was humming like a mill.

'Can't you wait for daylight to make such a racket?' the innkeeper went on. 'Just look, see what time of night it is.'

He pulled them out into the room, opened the window, and showed them the stars, for it was eight o'clock at night.

'Two o'clock, about. . . . This time, keep quiet, or we'll get angry. Since you want to leave so early, I'll come for you at cock-crow.'

He shut them up again in their cubby-hole, turned the key on them, and went downstairs to his friends. They were all laughing themselves sick and calling for more wine. No one slept at the Golden Lion that night, and a whole barrel of wine went dry.

The two tinkers slept as best they could, or talked together, without much sense.

'See here—aren't the nights long in these parts?'

'I was just going to say, did you ever see a place where they dragged on so?'

'Where they make you so hungry!'

'Where they make you so thirsty!'

'I'm sick and tired of it!'

'Come on, try and sleep again.'

'Sleep, sleep! I'll turn into a bear.'

They kept on mumbling their litanies, like a priest at a three-day procession. And the wags came up in their stocking-feet and stood with their ears against the door.

At last, at crack of dawn, the host arrived, rapped at the door and opened it.

'Wake up! wake up! It's the custom here to get up early! Yes, we don't lie late abed around here!'

And they had found the night long! They got up and ran for it as though the room were on fire. It didn't take them long to wash up.

'Could we have just a bite to eat?'

'And a drop to drink?'

'We're so hungry, so thirsty!' they shouted together, 'that this time we won't even think of the expense!'

'Eat and drink? Sure enough, sure enough: the room's full of folk who aren't as fond of their beds as you are!'

They served them what was left, the remains of the fair. If they had been served a wolf, as long as he was cooked, they would have eaten him. They cleaned all the plates, they drained all the bottles. In no time at all the word had gone over town, and men were still coming to watch them at it.

As for them, never had they seen people who rose so early, or in such a good humour, and so full of good-will that they got together and paid for the tinkers' dinner. What a dinner it was, and it cost them nothing! Never had they been so happy—happier than all these jolly fellows making merry around them. Even out in the street, where the laugh that went up when they left brought everybody to their doors. As for the tinkers they laughed louder than all the others.

'That's so,' one said to the other, 'no other place where the nights are so long. . . .'

'And, what's more, where they get up so early in the morning. . . .'

'All fresh and ready for a laugh. . . .'

'But for those who don't come from hereabouts, it's hard work to do as they do, and sleep tight all night.'

The Tale of Vidal Stout-Heart

ONCE UPON A TIME there was a boy called Vidal; his friends called him Vidal Stout-Heart. And indeed he carried on both work and play with a stout heart. Whether he was out in the dew of early morning, mowing, or in the town square on a Sunday knocking over the skittles, he put all of himself into what he had to do. Ploughing or dancing, singing, laughing, and drinking, he did it with all his might.

He was always ready to lend a hand to his neighbours. Light of step, free and easy, and wide-awake, gay as a gold-finch—everyone was in admiration before him, such a charmer he was.

His father had a poor little house with just room to turn around in, bench, bread-chest, two stools, and brown earthenware dishes on the table.

In this country there was a castle, in which there lived a

damsel of nineteen years, going on twenty. And about the castle were seven farms, all surrounded by walls.

The farmer of the biggest farm, knowing Vidal, asked for him to come and work by the day. Vidal did as was proper: he replied that he would be happy to come, but that before he gave his word he must speak to his father.

The same evening he spoke to him.

'Go ahead, my boy, they're good people. Our own land is small, there's too little work here for you—better you should go to them, they are honest folk.'

So there he was, hired out to the farmer, and it did not take him long to win their confidence. When they saw the way he went at his work and how gaily, they made him their chief hand.

At mowing or harvesting he was always first, and always with a song. Everything he touched went smoothly; people talked of him for seven leagues around.

The damsel of the castle, timid as she was, could not help watching him as he passed by, and she listened when they spoke of him. Even the old folk of the castle, the father and mother, found him worthy of praise. When they saw him with axe or sickle in hand, they told each other, 'Ha, that's a good worker! We couldn't have found a better!' And the same idea came to each of them, so that when they finally gave it words, they were already in accord.

One fine morning, before sending him off to the plough-ing, the farmer kept Vidal.

'Listen, Vidal, would you have a minute to come here on Sunday? Here at the house, then to the castle? The masters are asking for you.'

'Sure enough, if the masters want me, I'll come.'

'Listen, I'll tell you something. I don't know why, but I've a good idea that the masters are thinking of giving you their daughter in marriage.'

Poor boy, he was dazzled. When he could look at the

damsel without her seeing him, he was ready to eat her up
with his eyes. She had something, an air, a touching way,
that caught at your heart. But . . . No, he said to himself,
taking a deep breath, believe that they'll give her to me, that
I cannot.

'For what are we, my people? At home there are three
poor little cows so thin you can see their ribs, and a bit
of a donkey just strong enough to take my mother to the
fair. . . .'

'Just the same, better come on Sunday.'

'If that's all, I'll come. But I'm not getting any notions
about it.'

'Listen . . .'—the farmer wiped his face with his hand.
'All I say is this: maybe the masters want something of you.
You'll see for yourself.'

'That suits me, if I can do them a service.'

'I know you're not the sort to hang back. But—don't go
there without your stick.'

When Sunday came Vidal put on clean linen, polished his
shoes, and took his stick, a stout hazel shoot, supple as a
reed, hard as iron. When he had it in hand there was little
the boy feared to meet. He whistled to his dog, Whirlwind,
a dog who was quick and valiant like himself. Then off he
set to the castle.

The farmer had not told him much, but a word is enough
when you have ears to hear. Vidal was on his guard. All the
way, he kept a sharp look-out to right and to left: here by the
green clump of hazel that shadowed a fountain, there by the
hollow tree that rang to the tapping of a woodpecker. At
the most solitary spot in the road was a rock that he must
have passed many times without noticing that in its cleft
there was a sort of cave. That day—his good luck must have
willed it—it occurred to him to look inside. He stooped
over, and in the shadow he saw the face of a woman, a
woman with long locks of hair—peasant-women in those

days wore their hair cut short, like their men—looking at him without a word. Vidal greeted her.

'Good day, madame.'

'Good day, little Vidal.'

'You know me then, madame?'

'Yes, little Vidal, I know you; today you are as good as on your way to be married.'

Vidal was struck dumb. Then, red in the face, he rattled on, explaining with a sigh that there was no question of marriage, that, as he'd already told the farmer, it was quite impossible.

'By no means impossible,' said the fairy, 'and you will succeed if you go about it with a good will. The bigger the house, the bigger the storm that blows through it. It may happen that they have need of a stout heart to watch at the door and keep out the black beast—the wolf or some other monster. . . .'

'If I am to fight some beast for the damsel, there is none I fear!'

'The truth is, it's the beast with seven heads, Vidal; no faint-heart could stand against him. But you will overcome him, if you do all I tell you.'

She told him to enter by the little gate of the castle, not the large one. The beast would then attack him, but, with good courage, he should get the best of him.

She told him, too, that it would not be enough to kill the monster: afterwards he must watch out. And in a few words she told him what he must do.

So he went on his way. 'No faltering, now! Maybe the beast will crunch you up like salt—maybe he won't!'

His Whirlwind trotted beside him, close to his gaiters. His heart was pure, he put his trust in the good Lord in heaven, and he went ahead. Since the beast was after the damsel, he saw only that he must kill the beast or die himself.

He came to the little door, and knocked there.

And it was the beast itself that opened it, crying, 'You looked for me, you have found me! Woe betide you!' It leaped upon him, ready to devour him.

But he, you can well believe he wasn't having any of that.

The dog did not wait to be told; bold as a lion, he had caught the beast by its tail and had already torn off one of its heads, and then another.

'Come on, Whirlwind, Tempest, Hurricane, today you'll earn your name!'

The beast was made like a great serpent that wriggled about, a frightful creature; all its heads howled as though they would split their gullets, and darted in every direction at once. Vidal had hard work to protect himself with his stick, but that, too, was everywhere at once, and flew like a whirlwind.

Whistling and blowing, growling and yelping, the beast turned and twisted about them. Stout-Heart and Whirlwind turned as fast, but there was more than enough to do for both of them. Sprayed with blood, they were assailed on all sides with teeth and claws, as though tossed about by squalls and tempests, in a cloud of dust. Aha, Vidal! Lucky for him now that he was so nimble!

Attacking once more, Whirlwind tore off another head, then, like a stroke of lightning, two others at once.

All of a sudden Vidal saw that the beast had only two heads left. His courage rose high; he shouted to his dog, and the dog flew to the attack. Whirlwind leaped at one of the heads, while Stout-Heart, with a furious blow of his stick, beat down the other, the strongest.

After this battle, he might well have called them all to see. But he was covered with sweat and dust, wet with blood and slaver, his clothes torn and awry. Could he show himself like that, before the masters? Enough for now, he thought, pushing the seven smoking heads into a pile with his foot. As the fairy had told him, he cut off the tongues, wrapped them in ferns as though they were trout caught in the pool, and slipped them into his pocket.

Then he ran to the brook, where he washed Whirlwind, still panting, bound up his wounds, patted him, and promised him a reward. For his own part he bathed himself, rubbed himself dry with oak-leaves, made his clothes as neat as he could, and mended his torn breeches with three thorns. And there he was again, fair and brave, with a gaiety that won your heart.

As he still dared not to go to the castle, he went to the farm to comb his hair.

The masters must have heard something of the noise, for they were there, and the damsel too. What would have been her fate, poor girl, if Vidal had not killed the beast! Her eyes spoke for her. The boy had caught her fancy from the first day she had seen him.

He was not given to boasting, and had not much to say for himself. It was the masters who did the talking: after an exchange of courtesies and complaints about the weather, they approached the subject of their domains and then came round to their propositions.

At this moment there was a great commotion, and a splendid coach drove up, with coachmen, outriders, and footmen. Inside was a fine gentleman, with the seven heads of the beast wrapped up in his cloak on his knees.

So there! He knew how to talk, this smooth fellow, and he could have made them all swallow Tuesday for Wednesday. Who could have killed the beast but this gentleman? a young man of family, with more land and castles than he knew what to do with!

As for poor Vidal, he was very nearly shown the door.

And yet the young girl felt drawn to the boy. Timid as she was, she told herself, 'Can you let him leave without touching his hand, without a last farewell?'

She went out to find him, beyond the gates, under the

linden-tree. A word, a sigh, and then another word. . . . He grew bolder, and even dared say:

'As far as I know, there aren't many heads without tongues. How about those heads in the carriage—have they got any?'

'What do you mean?'

'Ha! yes, it's none of those fine gentlemen who killed the beast with seven heads. Whirlwind knows something about it. And right in my pocket I have the proofs.'

She put her hand on his arm, and made him tell her all the story. He, modest as he was, gave all the credit to Whirlwind; it was his dog, his good, faithful, valiant dog, who had done it all.

The damsel listened with her great eyes fixed on him. There was no more room for fear in her heart. She ran to her father, took him aside by the window, and told him how things were.

The father went straight to the carriage. He took the heads and opened their snouts—no tongues were there.

He turned to the fine gentleman, who came swaggering up, and said:

'Heads without tongues, I've never seen that in all my born days!'

They didn't tell the gentleman in so many words to clear out: they told him that they'd discuss the marriage next Sunday. It was a lie; but in high life they have to tell lies so they can get out of a scrape in good style. Besides, the gentleman had served them up a much bigger lie; the creature had the face to say that he, all by himself, had killed the beast with seven heads.

'Well, then . . . good day to you, and here's to the pleasure of seeing you again.'

When he appeared to conclude the bargain, the following Sunday, he found the door shut in his face. Vidal and the damsel were husband and wife, and both of them were off in the land of the larks, who are the same colour as the blue-bird, because they do nothing but sing in the air of yonder.

The Tale of the Learned Man and the Boatman

ONCE UPON A TIME there was a learned man who knew a million things. He could have told you what was the strength of lightning, the depth of the ocean, and the height of the sky. In a word, one of those brains that think they know how to revolve the earth and set the stars in their courses.

One day he came to our part of the country, and, to get a better idea of how the land lay, he hired a boat and set off in it from Jumeaux, on the river Allier.

When they came to the Wolf's Leap the sky grew lowering, and the boatman told him that it would not be prudent to keep on: the river at that place swelled very quickly to a torrent in time of storm and their boat would risk being swept on to the rocks.

But the learned man proved by three points that there could not possibly be a storm that evening. Then he began to ask a lot of questions about the river, the countryside, the weather, the season.

'I don't know much about it,' the boatman finally told him, 'but you, sir, it's your turn now; could you clear up the two biggest puzzlers for the peasants hereabouts?'

'And what are they, my friend?'

'Firstly, how does it happen that hens drink but never make water? Secondly, how does it happen that rabbits, on the other hand, don't drink but do make water?

'Pretty questions!' cried the learned man.

He set about answering them, and the words he used called for more explanations than his explanations themselves.

The boatman said only that he himself had never got bogged down in long words. It was enough for him to handle his own job. Keep a close mouth, see the practical side, and, whatever happened, never lose your head—that was his rule of living.

Gliding along over the waters, they kept up a lively dispute. And the learned man was forced to recognize that the boatman was a man of sense.

'What a pity, my friend, that you never went to school! Did you never learn any physics or chemistry?'

'Oh no, sir!'

'Well, for my part, I consider that a quarter of your life was lost there!'

And the learned man dilated on this theme: he explained to the boatman all the benefit that he might have drawn from these noble sciences: he would have known all about the waters, their currents, and forces. So many words that you would have wondered how anyone had room for them all in his brain.

'But, my friend, surely you have at least studied astronomy? . . . No? What a pity! Well, I consider that there too a quarter of your life was lost.'

The learned man was so full of zeal that he did not notice

how dark the sky was growing above the mountains; already the lightning flashed through the clouds. The river stirred uneasily, as a beast will do.

'And, my friend, how about philosophy, the great queen of science? . . . What, that too—you've never studied it? Well, I hold that there, above all, another quarter of your life was lost.'

He began to prove it, wagging his finger.

At the crowning point of his speech—they were nearing Saint-Yvoine—the storm broke. Thunder-clap after clap, chains of lightning, cloudbursts of water. In no time the river was swollen, and the current swept them away. The boatman tried in vain to stem it, but his pole bent and broke. The boat was whirled about; it bounced from wave to wave.

'We're carried away—we're heading for the rocks! Quick, sir, it's your turn: answer me, have you learned to swim?'

'No, my friend, I have not mastered that science.'

Hardly had he spoken when, with the full violence of the current, they were hurled against a rock. The boat cracked like a nut-shell and fell apart. Boatman and learned man were both tumbled into the water.

'You haven't learned to swim? Well, sir, right here you're going to lose the whole of your life!'

The Tale of the Three Hunchbacks

ONCE UPON A TIME there were three hunchbacks. Three, did I say? There were four of them.

But you'll see that later. To begin at the beginning, once upon a time, in a town on the river, there was a hunchback who was also a rich and powerful merchant. He was hunchbacked for all that, and as he carried his hump about with him far and wide in the course of his business, and heard endless silly jokes about it, he had not grown any easier to live with.

As a rule, hunchbacks are well-liked men in company; they are full of a sly and malicious humour, and can be most amusing. But not he; no, he was always snarling, and tiresome because he was so jealous. His wife was all that a wife should be, but he, aside from his hump, knew himself to be as ugly as a spoutless tea-kettle, with his red face, snub nose, hairy and knotted arms, and crooked legs. And so he was seized with fits of jealousy that drove him beside himself. Whether he was up in the mountains buying wool or down on the plains buying hemp, when the fit took him, back he must go to the house, on the gallop.

You can imagine how he looked when he arrived, the scenes he made. Once the madness had left him, all shame-faced, he begged his wife's pardon.

What a life he led her, poor little thing! She was still young and sweet, and as good as she was lovely. Virtuous she might truly be called, since she wished only well to her ungracious husband.

One day—it was in winter: he had stayed at home for the Christmas holidays—there came knocking at the door three strolling hand-organ players. They were all three brothers and triplets, each one a twin to his brother, and all three hunchbacked. Happening to meet in town over the holidays, they had celebrated the meeting around a bottle. Then, somewhat the worse for wine, they had hit on the idea of going to tell the merchant that he was their brother on account of his hump, and owed it to himself to entertain them.

Yes, they were bold enough for that. . . . He himself opened the door to them, for he would allow no servants, jealous as he was. The three hunchbacks, as they came in, presented their humps to him so that he might recognize their brotherhood, and they paid him their little compliment.

As luck would have it, that day he was in a good mood, and he fell in with the farce. He took them out to the kitchen, set on the table before them a roast of stuffed veal, half a roast goose, and sausages with mustard. And even, for dessert, pies and a custard. And he went to the cellar to draw them a jug of cool wine.

Upon my word, the three minstrels regaled themselves as it is likely they had never done in their lives.

When the last drop of wine was drunk, the merchant made them each a present of a whole crown.

After this he took them back to the door-step. There, once again as rough as a chestnut burr, he told them:

'I have always known that with my infirmity I must put up with a lot of japes and jests in this world. I have tried to make the best of it. Now, listen well: I mean what I say. From here you can see the river; if ever you come again to ask me for so much as a glass of wine, I'll have you taken up on that bridge and thrown off—and you'll find plenty to drink below!'

Having thus spoken, he slammed the door in their faces and went back to his wife. And there wasn't so much as a smile on his face.

From the room where she sat she had watched the affair, without hearing the words. But the look on the face of her terrible husband was enough, and the jerk of the hand with which he had chased away the three hunchbacks. Heads bowed, they had slunk away like poisoned rats.

The poor girl thought that her jealous husband must have been too harsh with them. 'I'll try to see them again,' she promised herself. 'I must make them some small present, so that they won't bear him any grudge.'

Some time after this, one morning the merchant decided to leave on a journey.

'Have no fear that I'll take another of my crazy fits,' he said to his wife at the door. 'This time you won't see me dashing back all of a sudden.'

'This time you'll do like the other times, when your jealousy comes over you. But do as you like—you can come back when you please, you'll find never a man at the house.'

'I know what a good wife you are, and I shan't come back any more—I promise and swear it.'

Off he went. All morning the lady sat sewing at her window. Towards noon, whom should she see crossing the bridge but the three minstrels. It came to her once more that she must not let them bear a grudge against her man, for, she told herself, the ill-will of any man to whom you have done wrong will harm you before God.

She rose and called to them. When she insisted, saying that the merchant was away, they finally came into the house. The lady questioned them, and they told her how they had come as a joke to call on her husband, how he had received them, and how he had sent them away at the end.

But they didn't tell all this like a man who puts his feet up and takes his time. Even though they knew the merchant was away, they could not feel at ease in his house. Every other minute, at every sound, their eyes went to the window.

All of a sudden they turned pale, they began to sweat, and all three of them jumped for the darkest corner of the room.

'Oh, lady, save our lives, now you have brought us here! Your husband is crossing the bridge!'

At this the lady grew whiter than her kerchief. In his blind rage the jealous husband would surely kill all those whom he met in his house. She saw only one way out: along one side of the room there was a great chest, and by good luck it was empty.

'Quick, my poor friends, climb into this chest!'

They tumbled into it with their hand-organs, hunch-backed before and hunchbacked behind, hunchbacked and hunch-chested, crooked hunchbacks, horny hunchbacks. 'Ha!' thought the lady, who was still young and simple, 'however do they manage to be so hunchbacked? Even my husband's not more so.' But she had no more time to think about it. Already her husband, full of wrath, was hammering at the door. She lowered the lid. Alackaday! it still gaped. She climbed up and stood on it, as though she were trying to shut a trunkful of clothes. At last the iron catch fell into its place, closing the chest; she flew to the door and let in her husband.

All afire with rage, he elbowed her aside, rushed into the room, and stared about him, stalking into every corner, peering out of the window. Then he grew calmer, lowering his hackles, but continued to pace back and forth. Though the miller's donkey carries the flour, he will always be black, the proverb says, and it was so with the merchant: all the kindness with which his wife strove to whitewash him had no avail against the blackness of his jealousy.

At last he sat down at table. His anger was still rumbling, no longer from jealousy, perhaps, but from shame. When the cat came to rub against his legs, he caught her by the scruff of her neck and sent her flying to the far side of the kitchen. The whole town would have trembled before him. And trembling most of all, his wife waited on him; since she had shut the three hunchbacks in the chest, she hadn't an idea left in her head.

Meanwhile the husband ate, took four or five good swigs of wine, and ran his hand through his thatch of hair.

'I am stark staring mad,' he said at last to his wife. 'They ought to throw me off the bridge into the river. Now I am going, and may I be thrown in for good if I come back before day after tomorrow.'

He took another drink, solemnly, to seal his vow, and off he went.

He had not reached the other side of the bridge when the lady, recovering her wits, remembered the three players. 'Ah, dear Lord, now I must set them free!'

Well and good, set them free! Only . . . the three players already had their freedom: they were dead. As dead as a door-nail. The hump of the first one was as cold as ice.

By great effort the lady managed to drag him from the chest. But she had no strength left to drag out the others. She felt that she was losing her mind. She could not stay there before this minstrel lying on the floor, as still as a stone. All bewildered, she ran to shut herself up in her kitchen. What was she to do with them, God in heaven, her three hunchbacks? She sat there pale and trembling before the mortal fix she was in.

However, as we all know, God helps those who help

themselves. Not knowing which way to turn, still in a daze, she went to the front door. Night was already falling. From Christmas to the Epiphany the days are at their shortest.

Just at that moment she saw passing by a certain waggoner, whom she knew by sight, for he came from her village in the mountains. A fine stout boy he was, built like a giant, and strong as a bull. Perhaps a bit simple, but, in his very simplicity, worthy of all confidence.

'The Blessed Virgin herself has sent him to me!'

She went out to him and told him who she was, and he greeted her with his best grace. He had come down that day on a carting job, and outside his village he felt somewhat at a loss; to meet someone from home put him more at his ease.

'Friend,' the lady said to him, 'will you do me a service, strong as you are? But promise me never to speak of it to a mortal soul.'

'Lady, for your sake, I'll promise.'

The tone in which he said it was a vow in itself.

'There'll be three golden crowns for you when it is done.'

'Lady, it's for your honour I'll do it, but three golden crowns could do me no harm.'

'What I'm asking you, begging you as a favour, for my sake, is to carry a dead hunchback to the river.'

'If that's all, it's soon done. Where does he keep himself, your hunchback?'

He went in after her. Turning away her face, she pointed out the dead man by the chest. The waggoner picked him up, one hand under his chin and the other grasping the seat of his breeches, and stuffed him into a sack. Without even hoisting the load to his back, he strode along with it to the middle of the bridge. There he upped with the sack and dumped out the man, who fell feet first into the stream.

Done and well done, and so back he came to the merchant's house, with the three golden crowns at the back of his mind.

'Lady, the job is done!'

No sooner had he spoken than he stopped, petrified. The hunchback he had just thrown into the river, that very hunchback, as far as he could see, lay on the floor, on the very spot from which he had already lifted him. For the lady had not dared speak of three hunchbacks. But now she had moved the second from the chest, the identical brother of the one who was floating down-stream. And she made as though to put three crowns into the waggoner's hand, beseeching him to rid her also of the second. But she could have spared her breath.

'Keep the three crowns! When I've done the job, you can pay me. But how did this knave manage to get out of the river? . . . Well, he won't have the last word!'

Again the waggoner picked up his hunchback, again he stuffed him into the sack, and in three steps and a hop again he carried him on to the bridge; and this time he threw him into the stream head first.

No, this time there would be no coming back. His mind at rest, the waggoner returned to the lady. 'Two trips for one man! Sure and certain, I've earned them, my three crowns!'

But hardly had he set foot in the room than what did he see, still in the same place, in front of the chest, as though he had sprung from the floor by magic? The hunchback, the same hunchback, hump on his back, hand-organ on his stomach.

'He must be a goblin! What, lady—you want to pay me? Wait till I've done the job first—you'll pay me then! All the same, I *did* throw him in, head first! And still, it's himself, no mistake. That very hump! That very hump!'

He seized him in a tighter grip than ever, without even bundling him into the sack. And he was ready to burst with indignation. 'So then, I'm to spend my whole night dumping that rascal into the water? Ha, this time he'll see if he doesn't stay there!' In a fury, he carted him off for the third time. He hardly felt the weight.

In such a mighty rage was the waggoner that as soon as he reached the bridge he held his minstrel high above his head, and shot him into the river like a log of wood. Then, for his own reassurance, he leaned over the parapet, trying to see clear. In the dark of night, amidst the foam and the eddying waters, he thought he saw the hunchback swept away with the current.

The waggoner straightened up and drew a deep breath, content at last. 'If he comes back this time, he's no more than a sorcerer. I'll say he's the devil!'

At that very moment . . . Ha, his eyes nearly started from his head. Right before him, what was that, taking shape again? As though he had simply landed on the opposite bank and was coming by the other end of the bridge—again, the hunchback!

In spite of all the merchant's fine promises, it had been enough for him to see a playing-card dropped by the side of the road, the knave of hearts. . . . 'That knave must mean that a blond young man is calling at my house!' All his notions seized him again, and jealousy made a prey of him. Immediately he turned about, and by this time, running like a madman, he was drawing near to his house.

What happened to him then he never had the time to realize.

'Dog of a sorcerer! Down you go there, back you come here! Devil or not, this time you'll stay!'

With a blow of his fist that would have split a rock, the waggoner felled the hunchback, caught him by one leg, swung him three times in the air, dashed him against the parapet, and then, good-bye, *bon voyage*, go see what it's like in the river!

'Just try to come back now—come on, I'm waiting for you!'

Indeed, he waited long enough for a turn of the clock. And this time the hunchback did not come back.

And so the waggoner went back to the lady.

'Lady, if you still wish it, I'll take the three golden crowns, and I'll say they are well earned. Four times I threw that damned hump in the river! The last time I caught him on the bridge, running lickety-split for your door. That time I fixed him properly. You can believe me now, you won't see him again.'

The lady's mind had been in a turmoil since morning, but like a flash she saw what had happened. She gave a great cry and fell down as though she were dead.

Perhaps she was dead in good earnest; the tale does not say. But, since the husband who was thrown into the river deserves small pity, we may as well hope that she found consolation. And another husband. Maybe one without a hump, but by all means one who was not jealous.

How Dullness and Wit
borrowed from Each Other

ONCE UPON A TIME there was a king, a gallant cavalier, with fine features, a good leg, melting eyes, and a noble air. And he used them all to advantage, the rascal, with the ladies.

For his sins he took the fancy, quite against his will, of a certain fairy of the family Carabosse. This fairy had never laid claim to being very good, but she had always thought herself exceedingly handsome. It was unfortunate that no one agreed with her.

You can imagine her surprise, her resentment, her anger, and her thirst for vengeance when she learned that the king had just married another king's daughter. Spiteful as a red donkey, she swore first to make them pay for this slight, and afterwards to become for all that the only wife of the handsome king.

Months passed by, but her oath held good. She swore it anew every morning when she got out of bed.

One day word came that the king was expecting an heir

within the week, or month at the latest. That very day she made her appearance at the castle, before the young queen.

'I haven't brought you my wedding present until today,' said she in a grating voice, 'but it will be one of the highest consequence. Know that, by my will, the son you are expecting shall be as ugly in face and puny in form as his father passes for a cavalier of fine figure and noble bearing. Thus my fairy gift to you, fate shall cause it to come true. Take that!'

No sooner had she spoken than she vanished.

The king and queen were bowed down with grief. All their royalty was of no avail; there was nothing they could do. The spell was cast. There was no help for it.

Nevertheless they made such an ado that at last they found a charming and good fairy to whom they might turn for aid. To make up for the gift of the bad fairy, this one wanted to give their son a welcome gift: that his mind should be quick, subtle, brilliant, keen, and joyous—a mind such as the good fairies have themselves, if you can believe those who keep company with them.

Shortly afterwards the son was born, and perhaps there never was son born to mother in this world uglier than he was. My word, a very monster of ugliness. If he had not been a king's son, they would have hesitated to christen him. As bad as that? Ah, yes, indeed! The queen, you may be sure, wept over it like Mary Magdalene. And the king, dumbfounded, could find nothing better to do than to spend his time far off in the woods, hunting wolves and wild boars.

The child grew older, and his ugliness grew worse all the time, instead of better. A face to frighten you. And so it did, because the neighbours' children who were called in to play with him took fright after a few minutes and ran away. Through the gift of Carabosse, the poor prince was ugly enough to make a mule shy!

The king, his father, who set a high value on good looks in a man, was so ashamed of his heir that in the end he repudiated the queen. And little by little, by enchantment or otherwise, Carabosse succeeded in taking her place. She got him to marry her, and was, to all effects, queen of the kingdom. She had a son by the king, and he was as handsome as the elder was ugly, but as stupid as the other was bright. Out of fear of the people, who had loved the queen and had never cared for this new one, she sent her child to be brought up far away from there, under the care of a neighbouring king who had only one daughter, as beautiful as an angel.

During this time Carabosse worked on the minds of those about her. Then, seeing that her son was already well grown, nearly sixteen, she sent for him. She showed him off in the streets, she was lavish with money and smooth words. Little by little the people of the country began to look with favour on the younger son rather than the elder, so easily is the world's eye caught by a pretty face. Cobblers and washerwomen argued it out on their door-steps. They said that with his hang-dog face the elder prince could never hope to become their king. It would make them a laughing-stock among all the people in the world. Oh, they were that sensitive to ridicule!

These protests were only murmurings at first, and then they grew louder. Finally the cry grew so strong that out of fear lest he lose his throne the king was obliged to send his town-criers to every corner of the city. They proclaimed that henceforth the younger son should be regarded as heir to the kingdom.

The fairy had laid her plans to betroth the new heir, her beloved son, to the daughter of the king under whose roof he had been brought up. She sent a painter to make a portrait of the princess, who surpassed all other girls in beauty. The portrait, done in delicate colours, was brought to the castle, where everyone could see it. The elder son saw it, and lost his heart.

'What have I to gain by staying here?' said he to himself,

his head in his hands, at the far end of his father's garden. 'Now that my rank of eldest son has been taken from me, I play a fool's part in this country. I must leave it, and go where I shall see the princess. There is no hope for me, I know, but no one shall guess how I long for her. If I must die of it, let me die, and it will not be such a sorry end.'

He left, and went to the other kingdom. He had no fear of death, and so one evening he made his way boldly into the castle garden. 'Ill-made as I am, the guards will take me for some oaf who has slipped in here to steal, and they will run me through with their halberds. But let come what may!'

He saw the king's daughter, a thousand times fairer than her portrait. Radiant and dazzling, with a charming, tender air that went to your heart.

Well, he drew near. Combining respect and freedom like a true prince, he paid her his compliments. But all she could do was to open her eyes as wide as moons, and, at sight of his ugliness, she turned toward a rose-bush.

'Take that cavalier out of my sight, or I'll become ill. . . .'

'You ill? Ha, princess,' murmured the prince, 'no one could find ill in you.'

He bowed, smiling, and, sick at heart, he withdrew.

It was with such a noble bearing that the guards, who had come running at the princess's call, stood at attention when he passed and saluted him, hat in hand.

He went on his way until he had reached the heart of the forest, where he threw himself down under a bush, covered his face with his hands, and longed to die.

His mother, the poor rejected queen, was dead, but the dead have powers denied to the living. The good soul whispered to the good fairy to come and help her child. The prince raised his head at a sound like the rustling of a leaf, and there he saw the fairy who had wished him well.

'Don't lose heart,' she said. 'The princess is as beautiful as an angel, but as empty-headed as a leaky pail. Do you know why? It is because she was brought up together with your half-brother. He gave her his dullness. Your turn now to give her your wit!'

Easy enough to say. If wit were as catching as measles, everyone would go and rub elbows with those who have it! And yet the prince felt comforted. In the days that followed he even dared again, with the greatest respect, to address the princess. But this royal maiden was far from ready to seek out his company. Because he was ugly she was more inclined to make him her pet aversion.

The good fairy took a hand, we may suspect. To the prince, transported by his love, she gave courage, even hope. While little by little the princess became used to enduring the sight of this grotesque creature, listening to his compliments, at first with curiosity, and then with a pleasure that opened her mind.

This news came to the ears of Carabosse, far off in the king's castle. She made all haste to send the younger son to the princess's side. But he had not been there three days when she took a dislike to him. Strolling beneath the lindens with the two brothers, the princess began to make comparisons. And she discovered that this handsome cavalier was nothing but a great booby. If he opened his mouth, it was only to talk about his horse—or else about his clothes: those he wore for dinner, for supper, for playing tennis, for playing cards. . . .

'Oh, of course,' the maids of honour said to the princess, 'he is not a great talker like some people, but he has such an air mounted on a horse!'

'I have no use for a great talker,' said the princess gently, 'but neither have I any use for a jockey. What it takes to make a man a good companion and friend is a clear head and a warm heart.'

'And chiselled features, an elegant form!' cried the maids. 'What a clown he is, that elder prince, Your Highness! His nose, and the rest of him! Yellow as a duck's claw, besides, and mottled with red like a turkey's neck. He's like a striped tulip from your flower-beds.'

'Take my eyes,' said the princess, smiling, 'and you will find him handsome.'

If at first she had made a monster out of his ugliness, since then, you see, she had forgotten it. Perhaps, too, as the game went his way, the prince grew less grotesque. Under the soft looks of his beloved, he took on an air of vigour, pride, complaisance: his eyes spoke, his skin grew clearer, his features seemed to fall into place. Even his figure grew more supple and graceful, with that easy bearing which is always a pleasure to see. As the princess had suggested, everybody began to see the prince through her eyes. And people no longer found her dull, because she had had the wit to think well of him before they did. Soon the prince and his wit were all the fashion: no one in the kingdom talked of anything else.

Since by then the king had died, they all begged his daughter to take the prince for her husband. They were so pressing that at last she consented—having made up her own mind to do so three months before!

When the bad fairy learned about this marriage, there *was* a to-do. Nobody ever knew just what did happen at court. It was said that she had poisoned the king her husband, that handsome man. . . . Perhaps in her rage she had cast a spell over him that turned out badly. Perhaps he simply up and died. There must have been an unlucky star about for kings that year. But it is likely that she had been up to some tricks, because the queen of the fairies changed her into a hobgoblin. . . .

Her son, the handsome cavalier, did not stay king very long at the castle. Where there is no wit, vice moves in. And he was a real monster of dullness. . . . Before the year was out, they could stand him no more, and they drove him out.

They knew how well thought of was the elder son; they called him back, and of the two kingdoms they agreed to make one.

Their young queen had beauty for two, and the young king had wit for four.

As time went on it came about that he took on something of his wife, so that he was no longer as ugly, and she took on a good deal of her husband so that she was no longer a goose. In this wise they lived to the end of their days, happy and content, surrounded by a troop of children, grandchildren, and great-grandchildren.

The Tale of the Murdered Packman

ONCE UPON A TIME there was a vine-grower who had a gay heart but a quick temper. His wife was often the cause of his flying into a rage. Oh, she's not the only woman who has brought this sin upon her husband. Every woman has her little ways, and hers ran to idle gossiping. She could never keep a secret. In the village they called her Thirteen-Tongues.

One morning the vine-grower learned from his wife that old Tripou, who lived on the market-place, was about to give up the ghost.

'His land will be sold,' he mused aloud. 'His vineyard on the slope, that would just suit me. It's been on my mind a long time.'

Hardly had they finished the soup when the woman, who got in a fever when she heard any news, ran off to tell her neighbour about it as if the matter were already settled. Yes, and before an hour had gone by the neighbour's husband had left for town, made an offer to the heir, and clinched the business. Feet will win the race, not eyes.

When Tienne, as they called the vine-grower, learned that

77

he wouldn't get the vineyard, and all because of his wife's babbling, his rage went on the boil.

'Ha, you silly creature! A piece of land that was just made for me, that joined ours. . . . See what you have done with your chatter!'

As he was a kindly man, he only treated her to two slaps and a few other light caresses.

'If only this affair would teach you a lesson! But what I say goes in one ear and out the other!'

All in tears, she followed him across the kitchen, wringing her hands, promising, protesting, and swearing that from that day on she would keep their business to herself, that she wouldn't say a word, ever again, to anybody.

'Swear, now? You swear it? Good, we'll see. Meanwhile, bring me out my morning and noon soup to the vineyard. I won't come back to eat, I've too much to do.'

'You understand, it was just a word I let fall, talking to the neighbour. But it's all over, really and truly. If ever again I let out one of the family secrets, I'll insist that you cut my throat!'

He, like a decent man, made a sign that he believed her, and that she could dry her tears. In the basket on his back he put a jug of wine, his tools, his umbrella, and the vine-grower left for the vineyard.

Towards eight o'clock in the morning, the woman poured hot soup in a pot, and, feeling somewhat lighter of heart, she set out for the vineyard. In the keen morning air, she made the trip in a few minutes, skirts tucked up in her pockets, pot in hand, basket on her head.

Once there, she set the pot on the wall, the basket under the peach-tree.

'Tienne! Where are you?'

She saw him higher up, stooping over behind the rows of vines, doing she knew not what.

'Come on now, eat your soup, before it's cold. Such a

good soup, with chunks of bacon in it!'

He straightened up and came down to her. She looked him in the face.

'Still thinking about old Tripou's vineyard? It worries you so much?'

He tossed that off with his head, as if now he had other fish to fry.

Truth to tell, he appeared less angry now than dazed, you might say, or frightened. His face was all askew, and his eyes fled before hers, shifted from left to right.

In short, a face to make it rain.

'But tell me, Tienne, do you feel ill? Or what's the matter with you?'

'Be quiet! If I told you, could you keep from telling?'

'You may be sure! Tienne, tell me! You can't leave me like this, not knowing!'

'No, I don't want anyone to know.'

'But I swear to you that I won't open my mouth! I swear it!'

'You see, wife, anger's a bad thing. Anger can make you do a black deed.'

'Oh, Tienne, what have you done? Tell me quick!'

'I'm coming to it. I'd only just unloaded my tools, and I was still a bit hot, thinking about that vineyard we lost because of your tongue. . . . Just at that moment, what did I spy? A packman, who came in sight between two plants, as though he'd come to sneer at me. My gorge rose right up. Those packmen, all they're good for is to damage the vines; there he was, that fellow, coming round just to fill his paunch at my expense. So then, I took hold of my spade . . .'

'And then, Tienne? Oh, what did you do?'

'I tell you, in a fit of rage. . . . Spade in hand, it only took one blow. I smashed him, head and all, I think. . . .'

'God save us all!'

'Yes, what creatures we are! And the shame that takes hold of you, when you have done the deed. . . .'

'But are you sure that he's really dead?'

'I couldn't be surer!'

'What did you do with him, my poor Tienne?'

'Don't ask me about that. I still had the spade, I dug. . . . And the earth's over him. You could walk over the spot and never know it. Of course, now, you won't speak of it. And so, as there was no one to see, no one will know. But the shame that's on me. . . . To think that I did such a thing!'

'He couldn't have had time to feel it. Tell me, Tienne, did he cry out?'

'Cry? Not a bit of it. . . . And you, watch out now, don't go blabbing it! Tut, my poor wife, let's talk about something else. After all, I might as well eat my soup.'

He caught up the pot in a kind of rage, and began scooping up his soup. And she stood there watching him. 'He killed someone. Tienne killed someone. A pedlar runs about all over the place: no one will know what happened to him. We need only keep our mouths shut.'

She would have liked to stay there in the vineyard—but no, she was afraid of the dead man, buried only three paces from her. She would have liked to run and shut herself up in her own house, but she knew that she could not keep still there. She did not know what she wanted.

She left with her thoughts eating into her head. From the road, as though in a dream, she saw men working on the vines, along the terraced slopes. One called good day to her, another spoke to her. Those who were nearest asked her if anything had gone wrong at the house. 'No? that's good. I thought you looked a bit peculiar, like a hen that's just found a knife.'

She chattered on to them about Paul, Pierre, and Antoine. But all the time a mill-wheel kept turning in her head. 'If they knew, my God, if they knew!'

'And my work waiting for me!' she broke out. 'If I stay

here gabbing any longer, I might as well be dead and buried. . . . See you later, Jean!' And she ran off.

Three pigeons circled above; men were tying up the grapes on the slope; a carriage rolled by; smoke rose from the town chimneys and dissolved in the air. Life went on that day like every other day. And if they had known. . . .

What a to-do that would have caused in the houses and the fields! She saw all the neighbour-women hanging on her words, their eyes starting from their heads, dumb, staring at her. . . . A long silence. . . . Then one cried out, then another. The murdered pedlar, the emotion over it, was like a fire running over the countryside.

My God, knowing what she knew, could she keep from setting them all in an uproar, those people over there who knew nothing, nothing at all? . . .

Where the road came out by the great nut-tree, she met her chief gossip, Tienne's own aunt.

She had to talk with her, with news burning hot on her tongue that would have had the power of a thunderbolt if she had let it burst.

All of a sudden she could stand it no longer.

'Ah, my poor aunt, ah me, didn't I fall down ten times along the road? I'll never live such moments again in all my life! . . . No no, don't ask me, I can't tell you. . . . Is it about Tienne? It's true, you're in the family. . . . Ha, I'd gladly tell you, but you must keep it a dead secret—swear you will!'

'Oh, my poor dear, if they killed me, I wouldn't . . .'

'Well, then. . . . But as though you were hearing confession! . . . Well, Tienne . . . he just killed a man. He found a packman in our vineyard, doing damage there, eating our grapes. With a blow of his spade, he split the man's skull. Yes, in a rage, you see: one of those that take him at the house. The pedlar didn't make a sound—nobody saw it. And Tienne buried him in our vineyard. What do you say to that?'

'My poor dear friend!'

'If you breathe a word of it, the judge will take my poor man and off will fly his head!'

They left each other. The aunt, in a fine state of combustion, ran to the house of a neighbour, her sister-in-law's cousin. She was afraid of a rush of blood to the head. No, she could not eat a thing—all she wanted was a bowl of buttermilk to cool off her blood.

She made a great show of mystery. But, since it was someone in the family, why shouldn't she tell? Another cousin arrived. There they were, the three of them, their heads together as though under the same bonnet, questioning, answering, whispering, exclaiming, questioning again, unable to make up their minds to leave each other, and yet burning with eagerness to spread the news.

From house to house the word ran like a fire. 'Tienne. . . . With a blow of his spade. . . . A packman. Yes, Thirteen-Tongues' Tienne. . . . In all the days of my life! And, above all, don't breathe a word. Promise? Nobody saw a thing, nobody must know a thing. . . . But he confessed it all to his wife. Yes, yes, a pedlar, no one from around here. . . . In his vineyard. . . . Tienne!'

The crime was on every tongue. Before evening came, they told of it from one village to another.

All of a sudden some boys ran up with the news that they had seen the gendarmes go by on their great horses, galloping towards the vineyard on the hill.

'Poor Tienne!' the men said, 'the law is going to cut his head off. Pity it couldn't have been after the vintage!'

Meanwhile Tienne was calmly eating his four-o'clock, under the peach-tree, knife in one hand, bread and cheese in the other.

His wife had just come back there; she had forgotten to bring his noon lunch; her head was turning, as you can well imagine. When she saw the black-hats arriving, she grew very pale. Her Tienne didn't look too put out; he greeted them with a nod after they had dismounted.

'You can guess what we've come for,' said the brigadier, stepping up to him. 'You are accused of the murder of a packman; you knocked him out with a blow of your spade.'

'I?'

'You! It's common talk, and you'd do well to confess and be quick about it.'

The poor woman trembled in every limb. Her eyes, as large as her fist, went from the gendarmes, whose sabres, braid, boots, and all flashed like lightning in the sun, to her Tienne, who went on eating his bread and cheese, so stupefied that you would have thought him quite calm.

'Do you deny what you declared to your own wife, here present?'

'Well! If I said it, it must be true.'

'So then, you confess that in a fit of rage you killed a pedlar who had entered your vineyard?'

'A packman.'

'If you like. And you buried him near by.'

'Buried? Well, say rather that I threw a little earth over him. . . . You're not going to take me to prison just for that?'

'What? For killing a man?'

'Who told you it was a man? I said a packman: that's what we call a snail around here. Wait—look here,' he got up, and with the tip of his sabot he pushed aside a little earth, 'here he is, the snail I killed with a blow of my spade.'

'A snail?' the brigadier said after a moment, and his crimson face burned as dark as a prison door. 'A snail?' Well, then, we'll turn in a report against you for contempt of the law!'

'All right, so be it! but make it in my wife's name, then,' answered Tienne, 'and in the name of all the women in the place: that would be even better! And if your report could stop their tongues . . . Come now,' he went on, picking up his jug of wine, 'let's drink to their health in my wine!'

'. . . The wine's not so bad,' said the brigadier afterwards, wiping his moustache. 'No use drawing up a report on the matter. In the last thirty years I've locked up many a fine fellow; I know there's one thing that they won't lock up, that they'll never lock up—and you know what! A woman's tongue!'

The Tale of Misery and his Dog Poverty

ONCE UPON A TIME there was a blacksmith whom they called Misery, and his dog, who followed him everywhere, they called Poverty. There had been a time when the dog's coat was as smooth as a silk ribbon, but he had become a mangy cur, snarling and filthy. And his master was like him, ragged and slovenly, as lean as Lent. He only combed his hair on Sundays, when he went to church, and then he used Father Adam's comb: that is, he dipped his fingers in the holy-water font, ran them three times through his crop of hair, and there it was, done for the week.

As for his food, he was just the opposite of his dog, who, if he had had any, would have eaten his meat without bread, while his master ate his bread without meat.

Even bread was not always to be had. In the morning he rubbed his eyes and went to look for a bite where he could find it. His credit had run out everywhere; iron for his forge was also lacking. Want had laid him flat.

One day the good Lord and Saint Peter happened to pass by his door. They were on their way to Spain, just like the pilgrims of Saint Jacques. The donkey on which the good Lord was riding had cast a shoe, and so they stopped.

'Will you shoe my donkey?' the good Lord asked the blacksmith.

'Yes, I'll do it,' said the other.

He looked about the forge for a piece of iron, and found none. Then he noticed the heavy silver buckle on his best Sunday shoe; he put it on his anvil, and in three firings he forged what he needed for the donkey.

'What are you doing with that silver?' the good Lord asked him.

'I am making a shoe for your donkey; I can't let you go along the high-road like that.'

In a minute he had nailed it to the donkey's foot.

'How much shall I give you for shoeing my donkey?' the good Lord asked Misery.

'Nothing, nothing at all,' said Misery, shaking his head, and he fell to puffing on his pipe.

'Since you want no money,' said the good Lord, 'make three wishes; what you wish shall be granted you.'

Saint Peter touched Misery's arm and whispered in his ear, 'Be quick now! Ask for Paradise.'

'There's plenty of time,' said Misery, 'for going to Paradise. Look, now: all the neighbours and cronies come and sit in my chair for a chat while I am hammering at the forge; then, when I want my place, nothing doing. Well, I wish that whosoever comes to sit in my chair has to go on sitting there until I give him leave to get up.'

'So be it,' said the good Lord. 'Two wishes left you.'

'Quick, quick!' whispered Saint Peter. 'Ask for Paradise!'

'I've time ahead of me,' said Misery, 'to think of Paradise. I keep a lot of patience in my pocket. Look, now: the youngsters who come to pull the bellows-cord for me, as soon as my back is turned, they climb my nut-tree in front of the door and steal my nuts. Well, I wish that whosoever climbs up my nut-tree will have to stay there until I give the word.'

'So be it,' said the good Lord. 'Only one wish left.'

'Ask for Paradise—oh, do ask for Paradise!' groaned Saint Peter, pulling him by the sleeve.

'Stop pestering me with your Paradise, you! Why should I worry about Paradise? . . . Look now,' went on Misery, tapping his pipe on his thumb-nail, 'I'm always leaving my tobacco-pouch on the window-sill, or on the anvil. Some-body comes along and takes a pinch of it, somebody else takes another. Well,' he ended, 'I wish that whosoever goes into my tobacco-pouch, can't leave it until I say the word.'

'So be it,' said the good Lord. 'The three wishes you have asked for shall be granted.'

He climbed upon his donkey, Saint Peter upon his, and the two of them rode away.

Nobody took Misery's chair now, nobody stole his nuts, nobody pinched his tobacco. But, with his three gifts, Misery was no richer than his dog Poverty. He who never took thought and let things go as they liked, he did think about that. 'I was short-sighted,' he said. 'I didn't even ask my own advice. What a fool I was! Where were my wits, to have asked only for twaddle and tomfoolery, not for riches? For next to nothing I'd sell myself to the devil.'

He hadn't long to wait. Riding up to his forge he saw a gentleman, a cavalier, who stopped, dismounted, and entered.

'Let's not beat about the bush,' said this gentleman. 'Just now, didn't you say that you were ready to sell your soul? Well, I will buy it, to be ready for delivery in twenty years. Until that day, you will find your pockets always lined with fair silver and fine gold.'

Upon my word, Misery had no scruples in sealing the

bargain. He sold his soul, and found that he could live very well on the proceeds. Nothing was too good for him to regale himself with. Feasting and junketing every day, as if the Three Kings of the Orient had come to visit him. And the food was nothing beside the drink. Along with his dog Poverty he went from tavern to tavern, and, more than ever, he preferred the mass they sang at the inn to that of the church.

Twenty years go by quickly when you spend them like this, among the jugs and the glasses. One day, Death appeared before him.

'Yes,' said Misery, 'I'm your man. Just give me time to put on my Sunday clothes and we're off.'

He hadn't changed his skin, at least—still tousled, and smutty as the bottom of the frying-pan.

'Don't be long,' said Death.

'Of course not: just sit down a minute, if you don't mind.'

He pulled up his chair to the corner of the fireplace, and Death sat down. Misery gave himself a lick and a promise at the smithy pail with the corner of his handkerchief. Back he came, ready for the journey, with his dog Poverty at his heels.

'All right,' he said. 'Forward, march! Well, aren't you coming?'

'I can't get up,' said Death.

'And you won't get up until I say the word,' said Misery. 'I'll say it if you will give me twenty years longer.'

In the end, Death had to give in.

Twenty years! At first it seemed to Misery like an endless amount of years. Days and weeks, they stretched ahead of him. But at last that skein of wool came to an end too. It passed by before he knew it, to the sound of songs and the clinking of bottles. One morning there was Death at the door.

'I'm not coming in! You won't catch me again sitting in your chair. But your hour has struck. Come along!'

'I'm coming,' said Misery, 'I'm coming. Just let me put on a clean shirt.'

To tell the truth, the shirt he had on was blacker than soot in the chimney. He started to pull it over his shoulders, humping his back.

'Don't come in, then, since you don't want to,' he went on. 'But, just to pass the time, climb the nut-tree, in front of the door, and try cracking a few nuts. You won't find any better in the country.'

Death, poor innocent, listened to him. And when the moment came to leave, with Misery in his clean shirt and Poverty at his heels, Death couldn't come down. He just couldn't.

At first he didn't at all want to come to terms, by granting twenty years more to Misery. But there he was, compelled to go on roosting in the nut-tree, like a hen on her perch! Can you imagine it, a world where no one died any more? No more funerals, no more legacies, no more new faces in offices or public positions. Gravediggers, lawyers, curates, and vicars would no longer know how to make a living. Soon there would be confusion everywhere, and an outcry going up to heaven. Death had to give in to Misery, and again he granted him twenty years.

And again the twenty years went by like lightning. A man with well-lined pockets, and no cares but how to amuse himself, can hardly find time heavy on his hands in this world. Sooner than Misery would have thought possible, the time came for a reckoning.

But this time it was not Death who came for him, to bring him down before the devil. It was the chief devil himself, and all the imps of hell.

He walked in as though he owned the place, with one glance at the chair and another at the nut-tree.

'You won't catch me with your tricks,' he said to Misery. 'Look here, at me and my people; you won't escape us. No excuses, now, and don't be slow, don't delay! We've got you, my man, and you're coming with us!'

'Coming,' said Misery. 'Here, Poverty! Come along! . . . Ah, if I'd only known, I'd have locked my door.'

'Your door!' snickered the devil. 'I don't give a damn for your door! Why, we can get in anywhere!'

'So that's how it is!' said Misery. 'Could you go through a keyhole?'

'Why, of course, and that's nothing at all!'

'Oh, oh, you're pulling my leg! You couldn't all get into my tobacco-pouch!'

He pointed at it, lying on the anvil: a pig's bladder, rather the worse for wear, which kept the tobacco cool.

'Look!' said the chief devil proudly.

He and his imps together shrank and shrank—they became smaller than ants. They swarmed up the anvil, they crawled into the pouch—and Misery pulled the strings.

And after that there was no getting out of it.

Misery was in a fine humour over having played the devil this trick. 'Now we'll have some fun!' he thought. He seized his great hammer, and gave himself the pleasure of beating the devils on his anvil, just as he would have beaten red-hot iron. It was a long time since he had forged with such a good will. The tobacco-pouch leaped and sizzled under his blows like hot cinders in water. Misery pounded on until his shirt was dripping. Then he thought he had earned himself a drink, and he went to get it.

But it was the same way with the devils as it was with Death: our confounded world could not get on without them. No more quarrels, no more lawsuits, no more battles. All the men who live by pettifoggery, lawyers and attorneys, were dying of hunger. They came to beg Misery on their knees. And he, like a good fellow, let go all those devils in his tobacco-pouch, after he had given them one more walloping.

The Tale of Misery and his Dog Poverty

Afterwards? Well, at last his hour came for good and all. Misery had to die in the end. With his dog Poverty at his heels, he set out on the road to hell. But when they saw him coming a long way off, the devils ran to bar the door. They didn't want hide nor hair of him.

Then, with Poverty, head drooping and tail between his legs, still at his heels, Misery took the road to Paradise.

Saint Peter came to open the door.

'So it's you, Misery? I thought you cared nothing at all about Paradise! When you could have it, you would have none of it—and now, it's not for you!'

In Paradise, in purgatory, in hell—nobody wanted him. With his dog Poverty, Misery went back where he came from. And that is why Misery and Poverty are still walking the earth.

The Tale of the Bold Cock

ONCE UPON A TIME there was a shepherd-boy who kept his two sheep on the hillside. And never was there a more good-hearted boy, more full of good-will, or ready to do a favour where he could.

It happened one day, as he was keeping his sheep, leaning on his staff and looking far away, as shepherds do, that he saw a shadow, a form, a hairy beast, glide from out of the woods and slip behind a bush in the next field, where a shepherdess was keeping her flock.

'Wolf, wolf, shepherdess! Wolf!'

He took off his sabots and clapped one against the other to frighten the marauder. But the wolf paid no heed. The shepherdess had fallen asleep in the shade of an oak; her dog and her sheep had done likewise.

The boy ran, barefoot, with no fear of thorns or pebbles—his feet were as horny as those of a beast. He flew to save the flock, without stopping to catch his breath, and arrived just in time. The wolf had caught the fattest sheep by the throat, and was carrying it off, slung over his shoulder. The boy arrived like a flash of lightning and knocked over the wolf with the butt of his staff, while the dog, awake at last, caught the wolf by the throat and strangled him.

'Shepherd, shepherd, how can I thank you?' How? she knew very well how, did the shepherdess, and her thanks came so warmly that the boy was moved by them.

'As a recompense, I'll give you my dog!'

Ha, if he had dared ask for her friendship besides. . . . But she had over sixty sheep, while he had two. He told himself that the dog was an honest recompense, and lost no time in making friends with him, out of love for the shepherdess.

Three days later he was keeping his sheep in the same place, on the hillside. All at once, over the mountain's back, he saw a storm rising. Castles on castles, mounting and swelling, invading the skies, purple as some venomous autumn mushroom, and blacker than mortal sin.

Far off in the valley he saw his shepherdess's father, sleeping in the midst of his hay, with all his help. The heat of noon lay heavy on the earth; they all slept, unaware that a storm was approaching.

'Storm coming, you haymakers! Storm right over you!'

He was not satisfied with cupping his hands and shouting: he ran until he reached them, just in time, woke them, and joined them when they threw themselves at their work. They raked, gathered up the swathes at top speed, and loaded the carts, while thunder growled, clouds scurried up, and the wind rose. A pity to leave good hay wet on the meadow, for it rots and turns to litter. At last they brought back the carts on the run, goading on the oxen beneath the first raindrops.

'My boy, that's a true service,' said the shepherdess's father. 'As a recompense I'll give you this cock, my bold cock, who hasn't his equal.'

And the boy dared not ask for the girl. All he had was a poor shack at the edge of the woods, a true Castle Tumble-down, where wind and rain entered as they would. The father was rich; he had a house roofed with curving tiles, a barn, and many good things—even a pear-tree against the front of the house, and the biggest manure-heap of the countryside.

The boy dared only blush and take the cock. Another honest recompense. And he made friends with the cock right away, for love of the shepherdess's father.

Three days later, on Saint John's Eve, again he was out with his two sheep on the top of the hill, along with his dog and his cock. The cock was scratching in the dry grass and brambles, pulling at them with his beak, pushing them aside with his spurs. It occurred to the boy that, as evening was falling, he would celebrate Saint John's Eve.

With staff and foot he made a heap of dry grass and thorns. He struck a light and set fire to them.

> Never seek to ask a reason—
> Fire is good in any season,

as they say, even in midsummer. Before going back to his shack, he sat there on a stone, watching the play of the smoke, the dance of the flames.

Suddenly he heard a voice, thin and whistling—he must have had good ears—the voice of a little viper with a golden collar, who shot up like a whiplash in the midst of the flame.

'Shepherd, shepherd, save me from the fire!'

And he had so much good-will, even for a viper, that he stretched out his staff.

> 'Viper with a golden ring,
> Save yourself a blistering!'

She leaped upon the staff and coiled herself around it, then darted up his arm to his neck.

He stood there pale and sweating. 'Ho, what have I done? Serpent of a viper! I gave you your life—is it death you are giving me?'

'No, no, shepherd, do not think me so ungrateful. Let me stay a minute around your neck, I am trembling—I fear the fire so much. As a recompense I will give you a great gift, which I can do only on Saint John's Eve. You need only do as I tell you.'

> 'Viper with a golden ring,
> What can be the gift you bring?'

'The gift of understanding the speech of beasts. Get up now, shepherd, and walk toward the rising moon. Take me back to the big pile of stones near your cabin. That is where my mother and sisters live.'

'And then, little viper?'

'And then, shepherd, my mother will ask you what recompense you wish for having saved me from the flame. You are to answer, "I wish to understand the speech of beasts, as I understand that of men." Such a great gift as that she will not want to give you at first. But you must be firm. I shall speak for you, and in the end I shall have it for you.'

He rose, with the viper around his neck, and went to the pile of smooth round stones that lay beneath the brambles.

The viper hissed, and as he stood he fell to trembling. There by his feet was a nest made of entwined vipers, that rippled and gleamed. They say that if you have the courage to bring this knot of snakes home it will bring you luck.

But the vipers reared up hissing, as though they would attack. Cold sweat ran down his back.

'Mother, sister,' said the viper, 'make this shepherd welcome: he took me from the fire, he saved my life.'

'My thanks to you, shepherd,' said the mother, the largest of the serpents. 'Since you have saved my daughter, you shall have your recompense. What do you wish for?'

'I wish to understand the speech of beasts, as I understand that of men.'

'Too large a gift! Ask for another recompense, shepherd.'

'I have asked for that one and I hold to it. Your daughter promised that you would give it to me.'

'My daughter promised too much in her fright.'

'Still, she promised.'

'Shepherd, this is a serious matter. It will give you more than you think. To understand the speech of beasts is to know the secrets of all things. There is no greater gift on earth. But since you have set your heart on it you shall have it. Only remember, shepherd—if ever you tell of this gift to anyone whatsoever, that same moment you shall die.'

And the viper blew into his mouth.

> 'Viper queen with golden ring,
> Thank you for the gift you bring!'

His voice trembled in his throat.

In a daze he went back home, and drank a great draught of cold water. Then he lay down upon his fern bed, but he did not fall asleep at once.

'A dog and a cock, those are honest recompenses. . . . But this gift of the serpents, now? I didn't want to seem lacking in respect before the viper—and yet, what good could it do me to hear my sheep complain that the grass is turning to straw on their hillside when I have no better pasture to offer them? Or even to hear the little birds out in the fields tell what weather it will be? By the way the clouds are flying, the blue on the mountains, the mist at their peaks or in the valleys, red sky in the morning or at night, rainbow at sunrise or sunset—by all these signs I can tell it as well as they can. How can it help me, the knowledge of the birds or the flocks? I have lived their life only too long. What I would like now is to build my house. Understanding the speech of beasts will get me nowhere.'

Turning over these thoughts in his mind, he fell asleep.

In the long summer days sleep is a sin. At first stroke of

daylight the boy went out in the grass, to see the sun rise on Saint John's morn.

As he passed by the heap of stones, he heard two little voices, and to his great surprise he understood what the vipers were saying.

'You can see his legs through the holes in his breeches,' said one.

'And his pockets are full of holes,' said the other, 'but I'll wager no crowns are falling out of them.'

'If he knew what was under his feet, this very minute,' went on the first, 'he would start digging with a will!'

The boy made a cross at the spot with the point of his sabot, ran for his pick, and fell to digging, and his hand didn't falter.

Three feet down he found a whole cask of silver, and then a cask of gold.

'Viper with a golden ring,
Thank you for the gift you bring!'

After that he could build his house!

And that was his first care, to build a fine house and move into it. There he was, with his dog and his cock. To the dog he gave a hundred sheep to guard, to the cock a hundred hens to rule.

'But,' he said, 'now that I have the castle, I must have a lady for it.' And so he dared ask for the shepherdess's hand.

Right away they gave her to him. And he was ready to love her through thick and thin, she was such a fresh and comely lass. She made you think of a bird when she spoke, as wide awake as a finch, and as full of dainty prattling as a warbler. It was a fine pair they made on their wedding-day, both ready to love each other and help each other with all their hearts, as a husband and wife should do.

That same evening, the new-wedded husband was in the

stable, grooming the horses for the night, when he heard the donkey say to the horse:

'A day will come when my master, if he wants to save his skin, will find he must learn to use a stick. Right on his little wife's back, he'll have to shower as many blows as ever I've received in the dog's life I've led!'

Yes, indeed, those were the very words of the jackass, and they sent him into a rage. He caught up a stick.

'Well, I can see you didn't get all that was coming to you!'

And that night the donkey got a fine beating. Well, what could you expect? A beast that went round saying that a day would come when he would have to go for his wife with a stick! His little wife, that tender blossom!

The next day he had quite forgotten the donkey's words.

And she proved a good wife, his little wife—only, the tip of her tongue was perhaps a bit too warm—it kept on the move, ready for an argument. And God knows there are always plenty of arguments lying handy about the house.

'A marriage made without chatter
Is no great matter,'

they say. You talk it over when it's being made, and once it's made it goes on talking. A household has to be well driven, and the wife wanted to hold the reins. Quick of tongue and easy to nettle, a bit hoity-toity, to tell the truth. She walked with her nose in the air and her eyes on the clouds, even when she carried the pigs their soup. What you might expect of a shepherdess turned lady of the castle. And he, the husband, full of good-will, let her lead him as she would. Really, she would have made him hold the cat by the tail all day and not twist it without her permission!

Riches had turned the girl's head. A golden belt is heavier than one of straw. And rich they were, no doubt of that. He who understands the speech of beasts finds he knows everything that is going on. The young fellow had bought one domain after another, to the outermost reaches of the countryside, and so he must spend his time visiting them to see that all went well. Off he went, mounted on his great horse, and, as she would not admit that anything could be decided without her, she went with him, mounted on the mare.

One evening they were on their way home after a long trip. The horse was impatient; he smelt the stable. But the mare, although her mistress whipped her with the bridle, hung back and trotted behind.

'What makes you so slow tonight?' the horse said to her, whinnying. 'If I were the mistress, I'd give you something to remember! Try to keep up with me, and don't be such a mule!'

'I'd like to see you in my shoes,' answered the mare. 'You only have the master to carry: I have the mistress and a foal besides. Just try it, trotting with all those riders! on top, inside, everywhere!'

The master, who had been listening to them, could not help laughing.

'What ails you, laughing all by yourself?' his wife asked.

'Oho, my little wife—just a notion that went through my mind.'

'What notion?'

'No, my little wife, that I can't tell you.'

She fell to pouting, more vexed than a cat when you take away the scrap she is eating.

'Yes!' the mare went on saying to the horse, 'it's easy enough for you. I only wish you knew what it's like to carry a foal. If that little scamp, instead of making me carry him, would get down and trot on his four feet, it would be a good riddance.'

The master burst out laughing again, louder than ever, and looked at the mare's belly, as round as a barrel.

What a rage his wife was in! To see her husband drifting

far away from her in a cloud of notions that he kept hidden from her—well, that she could not endure!

'See here! What ails you? Are you going out of your mind? What's making you laugh? Either you'll tell me or I'll be your wife no longer!'

And she set about him with her sharp little tongue—a tongue well able to unhorse a rider.

'Listen, my little wife, I am not allowed to tell you.'

'Not allowed! Well, since that's how you take it, I insist that you tell me!'

'If I tell you, I'll die that very minute.'

'You? You die? That's a good one!'

She went on working herself up to tears and reproaches.

'To think I agreed to be your wife, though I was rich up in the hundreds and thousands, and of a very fine family. And you, what were you? The shepherd of two sheep! A ragamuffin in a straw cabin ready to blow away!'

And having begun the song, she went on adding new verses. He kept his nose down. For in marriage there should be a sharing, and no secrets kept one from another. But what could he do? He could not tell her that one secret without losing his life. . . . A husband may well have a secret that he can tell nobody. At least it was that way in those days of magic, when a few could understand the speech of the beasts.

'Listen,' he repeated, not knowing how to get himself out of this fix, 'if I tell you, I die. You may be as sure of that as that you have five fingers on your hand.'

'Ha, you will die? We'll see about that! I've had enough of being a servant to whom you tell only what concerns her job. That's settled.'

'Well, since you must know, you shall know. But, that very moment, you'll see me die.'

Quarrelling and red with anger, they reached their house. The master rushed inside, and ordered them to bring his coffin. He had had it made when they were building the house, so that nothing would be lacking.

'Just set it down, so that I can get inside. My wife wants me to tell her a secret, which I can't tell without dying. My head is going round already—I can hear the bells ring. . . . So then, you will have it?'

'Yes, yes, I will, or it's the end of our marriage.'

'All right, I'll tell you. . . . Farewell to this sad life! But can you call it a life, with such a wife? It's no more than dust and ashes.'

He climbed into the coffin and lay down. The head servant put into his hands, as was the custom, a piece of bread and a penny. All the household wept and lamented. The dog was there, and the cock too. The dog was giving the death-howl, while the cock—cocorico! cocorico!—was crowing at the top of his lungs, as bold as brass. Just as when, perched on a cart, he was splitting his throat calling for daylight to show itself on the horizon.

The dog reproved him in his own language.

'Bold cock that you are! You dare sing before our master's coffin?'

'When the master is a fool, the cock can laugh at him. I wish I might wake him up, this man who's going back on his word to please his wife. He's quite willing to die, since there he is in his coffin, so let them carry him off to the nettle garden!'

'I say nothing of the mistress,' the dog went on, 'she's like all women—she has her idea and she wants to have her way. But oh, my poor master, my good master, so good that any flea that bites you is damned! Must a cock teach you a lesson?'

'Yes, and well I may!' said the cock, and he flew up to peck at the piece of bread his master was holding in his hand. 'I have a hundred hens about me, and not a single one of them would dare pick up a grain if I didn't allow her.

The Tale of the Bold Cock

The master should have started his wife off on the right foot. All goes wrong when the hen sings louder than the cock.'

And, bolder than ever, he sang, 'Cocorico! cocorico!'

All of a sudden the master, who was listening, remembered what the donkey had said on his wedding night. . . . 'A day will come when, if my master wants to save his skin, he will have to use the stick!'

It was as though the song of the bold cock had waked him up. He stepped nimbly out of the coffin and ran for the broom behind the door. He knocked it off its handle and the dance began.

He didn't beat her as if she were the miller's donkey, his dear little wife. But a good dusting-off, just as much as was needed.

> Cards, women, and salad, you know,
> Shake them all up, and the better they'll go!

'Oh, my husband, oh, my husband! What has struck you?'

'What has struck me? Why, that I'll strike when I like, and laugh when I like, too. Ha, so you want to know why? Well, I laughed because I was such a fool. But I'll prove that my uncle was a liar when he said, "When you're dead, it's for a long time, but when you're a fool, it's for ever."'

And, for a fact, he had decided not to die, and not to be so stupid.

He put back the broom on its stick and sent away the coffin. And everybody was satisfied—the bold cock, the dog, everybody. Even the lady.

For she didn't take it amiss to be put in her place. And from the day of her dusting-off she was no longer the woman who would rule the roost, but the good housewife who cares for her household and her beasts, sees to the daily soup and the salting-down for the year, the big wash-day in the first fine weather of April, the buttons on her man's vest. At the end of a drive-way shaded by elms, surrounded by their fields and their children, along with their dog and their bold cock, all went smoothly for them. No finer household under the sun. They lived long, happy and content, until the day of their death.

> And the bold cock sang loud and long,
> Cocorico, I'm bold, I'm strong!
> And there's the end of my song.

The Tale of the Child, the Snake, and Our Lady

ONCE UPON A TIME there were a man and his wife who had a little girl, as fresh as a cherry. They lived in an out-of-the-way corner, on the edge of the woods and in a marshy hollow, down by the reeds and the brown water. The wife caught a chill one evening at dew-fall, when she was overheated from having run after her goats, and the chill carried her off; in three days she died. The man was left alone with his little girl, who may have been ten or twelve years old.

To forget his troubles he saw only one way, and that was to betake himself to town in search of wine. All his money, and he had none too much of it, went to that end. He brought back a small keg in a sack on his back, and, as soon as he was at home, he fell to drinking.

Next day he had drunk the keg dry. There he was without a penny in his pocket, and in a rage because he could no longer pay for a bottle. The idea of working did not appeal to him: it was drink he wanted. But he who drinks must pay.

It came to his mind that the lord of money was Satan—

and he made no mistake there. So he put on his Sunday clothes, and on the stroke of midnight, in a spot that was known to be accursed, a cross-roads by a fountain, he made bold to call up the devil.

The devil appeared. He promised the man money, heaps of money, if that was what he wanted. But it had to be paid for, as you can guess. The man had to give up his little girl.

His poor wife's child, whom no one could help loving. No longer ago than yesterday he would have said that he loved her more than anything in the world. But today his heart was set on wine, and nothing else. To get it, he sold his child.

'And where must I bring her? Here, to the cross-roads?'

'Don't trouble yourself, I can very well come for her. Till tomorrow night!'

The man went home to wait for money to drink with, all impatience at the delay.

When night came the little girl went to bed as usual, and he too. They fell asleep—the child did, at least: the man slept as best he could.

On the stroke of midnight a whistle was heard.

'Get up,' said the man to the child, 'go and see who is whistling, and what he wants.'

The little girl obeyed him, in all innocence—her father had spoken sharply.

She took water from the holy-water basin, crossed herself, and went out. Three times she went around the house, saw nobody, and came in.

'What? You saw nobody! You're going back to bed?'

'No, no one. Perhaps there was a snake that slipped into the bushes.'

'Ha! you can't have looked.'

Next day, as he was going to the cross-roads for his orders, the man saw the devil rise up before him.

'When you go to bed tonight, throw away the holy-water

basin hanging on your wall. The holy water spoiled it all, and if you want my money you'd best take care!'

At his usual hour back came the devil, just at midnight. He prowled, he whistled. The man woke his little girl, and told her to go to the door, that there was surely someone who wanted something of them.

She got up as before, and stretched out her hand to the holy-water basin—but there was no basin. . . . She touched her finger to the tip of her tongue, crossed herself, opened the door, and went about the house three times.

'Back again, are you? Well?'

'Well, I saw nothing but a great snake who slipped away into the thorn-bush.'

Next day the devil came to see the father, and it was not good to hear him.

'Bring her by daylight, to the old bridge, four leagues from here—the one they call the devil's bridge. Don't fail, or it will be yourself that I'll come for.'

'I'll hitch the donkey to the cart, but it's a long weary way to the bridge! Where will I get the strength for it? With only a crust of bread left in the cupboard, and not a penny in my purse.'

'Once I have your daughter you'll be richer than the king!'

'But I must have money to buy wine, or else however could I bring her?'

'If money's all you want you shan't lack it.'

The devil spat before him, and it was all crowns of white silver. The man gathered it up and filled his pockets, but he wanted more, the wretch, and the more he saw the more he wanted.

Next day, early in the morning, he hitched up the donkey. The little girl asked him if he was going on an errand.

'Come along, now, I'm taking you to see your godmother. Put on your Sunday clothes? No, no, we're leaving right away. I must be back here soon, I have something to do.'

Sure enough, he must go to town in a hurry, once his pockets were stuffed with money, after wine. And not a bottle or a demijohn, this time, but a cask, a barrel, a hogshead. All he could think of was the wine ahead of him. The child he had so dearly loved, there before him in her little dress, with her clear rosy face, he knew that he was about to deliver up to the fury of the Evil One, but he never gave a thought to that. See, now, what a man's heart may hide, and what he may come to!

As for the girl, she watched him as he buckled on the crupper, and when it was done and he stood there embarrassed, hesitating to climb into the cart, she waited with her great serious eyes upon him. She had felt some surprise that they were to go on this errand, of which he had said nothing to her. But she offered no objection. She could not very well be joyous after the death of her poor mother, but she was well content that she was to see her godmother. The thought was very far from her mind that her father might mean to betray her. She was as simple as a flower from an old garden, one of those red or white flowers with only four petals.

She climbed into the cart and sat down on the wooden seat beside her father. The man touched up the donkey with his whip. They set off through the woods, down the dark and narrow road. She chattered on about her godmother, the weather, this and that. He spoke hardly at all, a word now and then. She said nothing out of the ordinary, only what a little girl growing up might well say when she was off on a trip with her father. And he felt her confidence, the trust she had in him, who was about to sell her.

At first she had thought that it was his loss and his sorrow that had sealed her father's mouth, and then she began to feel that there must be something else. She fell silent then, fearfully, and began to say her rosary, counting the Aves with her fingers.

They came out of the woods into a place where rocky

ledges jutted into the meadows, with here and there a huge old tree, the spread of whose foliage could shelter a village flock. There, standing on a ledge was a poor little chapel, low as a sheepfold, dedicated to Our Lady.

The child seemed to hear it calling to her.

'Oh, what a pretty church! Won't you wait for me a minute, so that I can go and see it?'

The man hemmed and hawed a bit. 'What can there be to see? No, no, there's no time.'

'Only a minute . . . just let me look. . . .'

'Be quick, then.'

She ran to it, but she looked at nothing, neither the windows nor the bell in the tower, nor yet the meadow pinks and pansies, nor the spring that bubbled in a grassy hollow. She pushed open the door, ran in, and knelt on the stone floor.

At the same moment she saw before her a lady, more dazzling and pure than the sun.

'Where are you going, my child?'

'I am going to see my godmother, my Lady.'

'My child, you have been misled. No, it is not to your godmother that they are taking you. You will stay here, in my place, and I shall take your place, in your father's cart.'

And so it was done. So wondrously done that the man suspected nothing. As soon as she who had taken on the semblance of the little girl climbed into the cart, he whipped up the donkey. The road led down to the steep cliffs that overhung the river. At every stop they met sharp turns and crumbling footholds; down below, the water plunged and boiled into whirlpools; above were trees that clung to clefts in the rock. On they went, and the road grew wilder all the time. The man spoke not a word. At last they saw the bridge, a donkey-back bridge with a hump like the point of an A— so dizzily swung across the torrent that it must have been the work of the Evil One.

At the last turn in the road the father pulled up the donkey, for he saw that there was someone on the bridge, waiting for the bartered child.

And the child, or rather, she who had the semblance of the child, with no question, no word of surprise, stepped lightly down from the cart. She walked out on the bridge, showing no sign of fear, even when the black demon sprang upon her. Just as he was about to seize her she held out her hand.

The other was flung backward as though he were a ball. A ball, or a leaf swept in a hurricane—over the railing, helter-skelter, head over tail, down he went, to crash at the bottom, far below, among the rocks and the spray.

The man did not understand what his eyes had seen, but a change took place in his soul. She whom he took for his child came back to him, and climbed into the cart before, trembling as he was, he could utter a word. It was she who spoke to him.

'Now,' was all she said, 'we must go home.'

As though in a dream, he urged on the donkey. Then, at a word, he came to a halt before the chapel.

He did not suspect that she who came back from it was not the same as she who had just returned to it, and whom he had taken for his daughter. But he felt that a change had taken place in himself, and he could not have told why.

Back they both went to their house in the woods. He emptied his wine-bottle into the marsh, he emptied his purse on the dung-heap. And there beside his little girl a new life began for him—a life of hard labour and deep faith.

The Tale of Squeeze-Penny and the Devil

ONCE UPON A TIME, in Corquelicande, there was a rascal. Corquelicande is such a good town that they only have a rascal there once every hundred years. But this time Corquelicande had its rascal all right. He was one of those usurers who pile up grain in their lofts so that they can sell it for double the price in time of dearth. Crookeder than a thorn-bush, and tougher than old leather. They called him Squeeze-Penny, and it suited him. When it came to dealing with him, they had just as lief deal with the devil. And what is more, word had gone around the countryside that he was hand in glove with the devil.

One morning, Squeeze-Penny left his house, with a note that had just fallen due in his pocket. Out on the road he met his partner, already off on his day's rounds, skipping along in fine fettle with a sack on his back, like a pedlar of rabbit-skins.

'Well, well!' said Squeeze-Penny. 'Going to the fair?'

It was the fair of Saint Laurence, which falls on the tenth of August. But Squeeze-Penny was mindful of his manners;

in spite of that little affair of the gridiron, he was not going to mention Saint Laurence to the devil.

'Looks like it,' said the other. 'Not that I'm counting on finding much in the way of business, but, all the same, I've got to go and take a look.'

'Oh, well, at a fair there'll always be some pickings—so many pints being drunk, so many tall tales flying around. . . .'

'Yes, and where does that get me?' said the devil contemptuously, and he spat in the dust and rubbed his foot over it. 'If I'd had anything better to do this morning, I'd never have set foot in these backwoods.'

'Fairs aren't what they used to be.'

'Like everything else. I wouldn't even earn the nails of my sabots there, if I wore any.'

They walked along together, side by side, talking of this and that until they came to an inn.

As they were passing they heard a great bustle and hullabaloo. It was the landlady, berating her little boy.

'You scamp you, you deserve a . . . How often did I tell you not to open that cupboard? And now the cat's stolen my roast. Oh, oh, the devil take you!'

'Well,' said Squeeze-Penny, coming to a stop, 'there's somebody offered you; aren't you going to take him?'

'Offered, great Lucifer!' said the devil, shrugging his shoulders. 'Do you think that she means business?'

He spat in the dust again, and rubbed his foot over it.

Both of them figuring things in their heads—the devil is always figuring—they went on their way. Squeeze-Penny pulled the note out of his pocket, looked it over, nodded his head and told himself that the sum was correct.

The devil asked to see it, and Squeeze-Penny explained the business. It began five years ago: a certain widow with six children to raise had borrowed thirty crowns from him to buy turnip seed, and sabots and the like for her little ones. Thirty crowns had only brought ten per cent interest, but

The Tale of Squeeze-Penny and the Devil

Squeeze-Penny had added a renewal fee of five crowns; the year after the widow had borrowed fourteen more crowns off him. What with the two loans with interest, and interest on interest, she now owed him one hundred crowns. If she did not have them, she would see if Squeeze-Penny did not take over her house and land.

The devil whistled, folded the paper, and gave it back.

They came to a fork in the road. 'See you later,' said Squeeze-Penny. 'I turn this way.'

But in a field beside the road they heard a row that stopped them in their tracks. It was a man and his wife, only married that year, out planting turnips.

> When Saint Laurence comes around,
> Put your turnips in the ground.

He was sowing the seed, and she was covering it up with the back of her rake. He did not like the way she went at it, and so he was giving her what for, and she was giving him the same.

'You stubborn mule!' cried the man, 'the devil take you!'

'Let him take you!' cried the woman, 'twin brother of a mule, great red donkey!'

'Well,' said Squeeze-Penny, 'two at once: why don't you scoop them up this time?'

The devil only shrugged his shoulders. 'That's all hot air! Think they can fool an old hand like me? Five minutes from now, they'll be sitting by the hedge, eating their lunch, better friends than ever. The racket they make is like the song the landlady was singing to her boy. All I can put in my sack is what is given me in good earnest, from the heart. . . . But here, since you're going that way, for friendship's sake, I'll come along with you. Let's go and see the widow.'

So they went.

Knock, knock, knock.

Squeeze-Penny, note in hand, waited at the door.

'Greetings, mother.'

'Greetings. And what do you want?'

'You know well enough. Just my little account here. It's due today. Pay me a hundred crowns.'

'A hundred crowns! I borrowed forty-five, and not quite that! Pay back more than the double? One hundred crowns, now! Rascal, bandit, bloodsucker of the poor! The devil take you!'

She turned to reach for the broom. . . . When she faced about there was nothing there. Nothing but a smell of sulphur, and a small whirlwind of dust, going down the road.

For this time what had been given the devil was given in earnest. He had only to take her at her word.

Quicker than lightning, he had caught up his friend and had stuffed him in his sack. No one knows what he did with him, but Squeeze-Penny was never seen thereabouts again.

The Tale of the Two Millers and the Charcoal-Burner

ONCE UPON A TIME there was a charcoal-burner who, to fulfil a vow, set off on a pilgrimage to the shrine of Saint Jacques. On the road he was joined by two millers. All three of them put their provisions into one sack, and, as the charcoal-burner stood first in height and brawn, the honour of carrying it usually fell to him.

Two millers and a charcoal-burner make three pilgrims with a good appetite. And the road was a long one—the shrine of Saint Jacques is off at the other end of Spain. Before they reached it their victuals ran short. Once at the shrine they would find enough to fill their sack, but, in the meantime, its two sides were sticking together. All that was left at the bottom was three handfuls of flour and as much butter as would make three walnuts. The two millers were as thick as thieves at a fair. They saw that their companion was a simple, honest man—just the man to play a trick on.

'Now,' said one of them, 'we must make a cake.'

'Only,' sighed the other, 'it won't be a big one.'

'If we divide it in three,' his comrade went on, 'such a small mouthful can only whet our appetites.'

'I don't know what's the custom among charcoal-burners, but in such a case we millers see to it that one of us eats his fill, and his comrades, for friendship's sake, go without. Isn't that the best way?'

To tell the truth, the two of them had decided to eat the cake themselves.

'Yes,' the first agreed, 'sharing the cake would only make a bite for each—it must go to one of us.'

'Just what I think,' declared the other.

'But,' asked the charcoal-burner, 'who will get it, then?'

'Heaven will decide,' answered one miller. 'Let it go to the man who has the finest dream tonight.'

'That's a good idea and I'm in favour of it,' assented his comrade.

After this there was not much that the charcoal-burner could say.

Night fell, and the three men came to a halt, under a great oak. The charcoal-burner built a fire of twigs and dry wood; one of the millers went for water from the brook, while the other mixed the cake and put it to cook under the ashes.

This done, they rolled themselves up in their cloaks for a nap, as they had agreed, since the cake could only be eaten after they had slept and dreamed.

But the day's march had been a long one. Hardly were the millers stretched out upon the heather than a deep sleep fell upon them. There they both lay, snoring like bell-ringers. The charcoal-burner listened to their snores; it seemed to him that there was something better to do. A whiff of hot bread came to his nose; such a dainty cake . . . oh! faith, what a fuss about it! He himself was a man of few words. He got up, and if only the millers had wakened then they would have seen him swallowing the evidence. But he did not wake them up, and when he had done he lay down and fell asleep.

At break of day the millers opened their eyes and shook themselves, spurred on by the thought of the cake. Some say that sleep is as good as a dinner, but they had not found it so.

'Listen, comrades,' said the first, when he had cleared his throat, 'while I tell you of my dream. Two angels caught me up, and flew away with me. High up they carried me, until I could look down and see the whole of hell itself!'

And he spun a fine yarn, of lakes of flaming pitch, rivers of hot coals, demons running about like ants, turning the damned on their forks in swirling gusts of flame—you would have wondered where he had come across all that. But the other, too, was in a hurry to tell his dream.

'Aha, I too; two angels came and caught me under the arms, and carried me high up in the middle of the air. Only it was a trip over Paradise they took me on. What wonders I saw! Such groves, such arbours, such gardens in full bloom. . . .'

Eager to outdo the other, he spun his yarn. All about them he spread pink clouds, rainbow mists, perfumed breezes, and flying cherubim. Both of them wanted that cake.

Carried away by their own words, they had not noticed that the charcoal-burner was still sleeping, as though their stories were lulling rather than rousing him. At last the two millers had to shake him by the shoulder.

'Ho!' he cried, 'must you wake me out of a sound sleep?'

'Comrade, remember our pact. Time for a dream now, not for sleep. The cake to the best dreamer!'

'Well, but I don't know if I dreamed or not,' said the charcoal-burner, rubbing his eyes. 'All I know was that— this will make you laugh, now!—both of you went whirling away through the air, one to hell, the other to Paradise. As for me, I stayed right here, like a great booby, telling myself that I'd never see you again. So then, in a dream maybe—I can't tell for sure—well, look under the ashes and you'll see for yourselves—I got up, and I ate the cake.'

The Tale of the Devil and the Peasant

ONCE UPON A TIME there was a man, a peasant, who was short of money, but had plenty of courage, stout arms, and good-will. For a handful of money he bought himself a farm, and a pretty good one at that—quite a stroke of luck. You could raise a bit of everything there, except grapes—it was too high for that. It was well up in the hills, with a lot of pastures and woods about it, off at the end of nowhere. The kind of place where, as they say, the good God only passed by twice—once to make it, once to say goodbye to it. There had been things whispered about it, from mouth to mouth. Yes, but as for him, he was not looking for trouble. A good farm like that, to be had for a song! . . . Ha, just let him settle there, lord of his lands! By God's help, he would know how to get rid of trouble if it crossed his path.

So he bought his house, furnished it, and moved in with his wife. That was one thing he had to have, sure enough— it is the wife that makes the house. This one was all that he could want. Plump and well-rounded, lively as they come—quick as a partridge, busy as a bee.

All this happened in summer, not long before Our Lady's day in August. At crack of dawn he was up and out, a tough little fellow, ready for anything, heading straight for the day's work. He went through the hedge, and stood there, looking about his land.

He had not been there a minute when the sound of a twig cracking—or perhaps it was just his idea—made him turn his head. And right beside him there stood a tall gentleman, looking him over with a pair of eyes that shone like candles.

'Well, boy?' said this personage, just as an over-lord would speak to his farmer, 'well, boy, what do you mean to plant for me here on this land?'

'Faith, my good sir,' said the peasant, nonplussed, 'I only bought it yesterday, but since it's *my* land'—he stressed the *my*—'I'll try to do my best with it.'

'Your land! *Your* land? That was how they sold it to you, perhaps, but in that case the seller fooled you. In these parts there's only one master, and that's myself.'

And the warning came in such a tone, my friends! The words cracked like pistol-shots. Such eyes, such a look! Even the air smelled scorched round him.

'But come now!' he went on. 'You look as though you knew how to till the ground. I'll take you for my farmer. You'll have no trouble with storms or hail; but mind, now, when the time comes, we share the crop.'

'All right,' said the peasant, showing no surprise, 'but before talking about crops we must make our covenant. What do you take for your share: what's on top of the ground or under it?'

'What's on top,' said the tall gentleman.

Well and good. The peasant, as was fitting for the season, planted turnips. When the time came to dig them, he went out with his cart. The devil came too. The covenant was made, and well made. The peasant took his knife, and in a trice he had cut off all the turnip-tops. There they were, to each his share: a heap of turnips for the peasant, a heap of tops for the devil.

Devil and peasant went to sell their goods in market. By evening one had cash in his pocket, the other had collected only grins, and enough of those to fill a double sack if he had wanted.

'You've tricked me,' said he to the peasant, 'but you won't trick me twice. Next year, what's on top is for you, what's under the ground for me.'

Well and good. The peasant planted barley. He had nothing to complain of with the weather. Time came for harvesting, and the devil was there. According to the covenant the peasant had the sheaves for himself, the devil got the stubble.

Again they went to market. You can guess how that turned out. All day long everybody was laughing at the devil with his cartful of stubble for sale. By evening he was ready to burst with anger.

'Ha! you rascal! You tricked me again, but I'll fix you! Next year I'll take for my share both what's on top and what's underneath.'

Well and good. Next year the peasant planted pole beans. When the beans were ready, he picked them, and when the devil came for his share he got both roots and beanstalks.

When he came back from the fair that night he was choking with fury, red as hot coals, puffing and growling.

'See here!' he said to the peasant, 'this kind of sharing can't go on. It's got to be clear whose farm this is. This is what we'll do: tomorrow morning at sun-up we'll meet at he devil's bridge.'

'And then?'

'Each of us is to come there, riding on some beast, any he pleases. If I can guess what your beast is, I get all the crops and you all the work. If you can guess mine, you keep the property; I'll leave it to you free of charge, without storms or hail.'

Well and good. There was no arguing with the devil.

Next day, before dawn, the peasant made his wife get up and take off her shift; then he smeared her all over with honey, from her hair to the soles of her feet; then he rolled her in down from a feather-bed ten or twenty times over, and more. She was a well be-honied and be-plumed woman, like an enormous ball of feathers. He then tied a donkey's tail on her so that it hung down over her nose, put a bridle on her, and off they set for the devil's bridge.

The peasant had made haste so as to get there before sun-up. He and his wife went down and hid themselves under the bridge, among the reeds and the bushes. There they waited until the devil and his beast should appear.

At last they saw him; he came down the road, his steed trotting gently along.

His steed? Well, you've heard of the dahu, the beast who gallops up trees with horses' hooves? And you've heard of the chabirou, who has two feet on one side shorter than the two on the other, so that he can run along the side of a mountain? The devil's steed was more of a phenomenon than dahu and chabirou put together.

The devil was riding astride, his legs dangling. To arrive in style, he put his mount to a gallop, in spite of the hill and the donkey-back bridge. He dug his heels in the beast's belly and, just as you shout 'Giddap, horsy!' he shouted 'Giddap, Ricalon of Bigorne!'

With that the peasant, on the other side of the bridge, straddled his wife, and they set off across the bridge, capering along.

At the high point of the bridge the two riders came face to face.

'Hey there! Greetings! Here I come, I too!'

'So it's you? Greetings, my good fellow!'

Right on the dot, the sun rose. Time to decide whose was the farm.

'Lord love me! said the peasant, hardly glancing at the devil's beast, 'had you nothing rarer than that in all your stable? My poor sir, you can't win!'

'And when did you ever see a beast like this one?'

'Hang it! all the little tots learning their ABCs know it as well as they do the donkeys, or the pigs, if you'll excuse me, that they see in market.'

'Can you tell me his name?'

'Every brat knows it: it's a Ricalon of Bigorne. . . . All right, your turn! See if you can guess the beast I'm riding.'

The devil was as flabbergasted as if horns had sprouted from his backside. He climbed down from his steed, walked round that of the peasant, looked in its face, sniffed at it, prodded it with his finger, and round it again.

'What sort of a kind of an impossible beast is that? Neither front nor rear, since it has a donkey's tail instead of a muzzle, goose feathers, and four legs. Who ever saw such a creature? . . . Oh, go on, keep your farm! Never again will I set foot in a place where you see things more frightful than anywhere else in the world!'

And so saying, crestfallen enough to lower his horns, he turned on his heels, mounted his beast, and galloped off so fast that in no time he was out of sight. And, just as he had said, in those parts he was never seen again.

The Tale of Take Him or Leave Him

ONCE UPON A TIME there was a parish priest in a small town who, on the morning of every holy-day, was at the church to hear confession. On Saint John's Day, at mid-summer, the cobbler's widow came to him, and when she had recited her sins she asked his advice.

She told him that her husband had had a helper, an honest and faithful workman, well skilled in the cobbler's trade, and that without this young man she would already have been forced to close the shop. Would it not be better, now, for her to form an attachment—to marry him?

'Marry him? All right,' said the *curé*. 'Go ahead and marry him.'

'But, you see, I'm afraid of his getting the upper hand. Suppose my man should become my master?'

'That would be a great pity,' said the *curé*. 'By all means, don't marry him.'

'But what can I do? Keeping the business going is too much for me, if I have no one to manage the shop. And who better could I find than he?'

'Then take him,' said the *curé*.

'But if the marriage turned out badly? What if he laid hands on all that's mine, made light of me, and gave me no comfort nor peace at home?'

'Then don't take him,' said the *curé*.

'Yes, but then what will become of me? 'Twould be an even surer thing then, all my money would go astray.'

In this way they argued it back and forth for over a quarter of an hour; not being able to get up her courage, she couldn't make up her mind.

At last the *curé* saw where the shoe pinched, and that she really wanted this marriage. He came near telling her, 'Take him, then, if you've got him in your blood, and no more arguments, since you've settled it!'

She was there, he saw, not for advice but for approval. And could he approve? To him, this second marriage looked none too promising. He studied her face, lean and pinched, yellow as roast pork—what you would call a widow getting on in years—and said to himself that if the young man wanted the good dame, it could only be to have the shop for himself. But, if he told her so, would she listen?

She was still weighing it, for and against.

'To make him, the workman, the master. . . . On the other hand, without a man in the house, poor me, what can I do?'

Just then, high up in the bell-tower, the bells began to ring for the holy-day.

'There,' said the *curé*, in a solemn voice, 'listen to what the bells tell you, and do as they say.'

The good dame went out of the confessional, listening with all her ears.

And the bells sang as they swung:

> Hear our song—
> You shall wed,
> Take him to your board and bed—
> Your husband,
> Your husband!

The Tale of Take Him or Leave Him

It didn't take her long to hear that, nor was she long in marrying the young shoemaker.

But no more did it take the sly fellow long to get the upper hand, just as she had feared. At the end of three weeks, without his permission, she would not have dared twist the cat's tail. She had been the mistress, she became the servant. And if she fell to groaning, crying, and complaining, he caught up a strap and gave her a belting, letting it fall on her back or hind-quarters, it made little difference to him.

When it came to Saint John's day in winter she could stand it no longer. She went back to see the *curé*, and this time she was full of reproaches.

'Well, I can see now what this has brought me! A curse on the hour and the day and the year when I followed your advice!'

'Advice?' replied the *curé*. 'Did I give you any? What I told you was to listen to what the bells were saying. Listen to them now—what do they say?'

The sacristan had just set them ringing. She listened. And this time sorrow had opened her ears, and she heard:

> You were wrong
> To be wed—
> Now he rules your board and bed,
> Your master,
> Your master!

The Tale of the Nail

ONCE UPON A TIME there was a poor countryman who, in his youth, had often heard his father and grandfather say, 'Waste not, want not,' and 'You can find a use for everything if you try.'

> Save a nail, bad or worse—
> Some day it may fill your purse.

That year the winter had been long and hard; loft and larder were not too well stocked. Spring was returning with its green shoots and its cowslips, and the roads were open once more. But those are hard months to weather, with the flour-sack empty and the purse likewise.

One morning the man set out for town, telling himself that he would surely find work to turn his hand to, so that he could bring back a loaf of bread and a side of bacon for his wife and children.

He was trudging along the high-road when a cavalier rode past him, a gay young blade on his way to rejoin the army, well mounted on a horse whose coat shone like a silk ribbon. His steed trotted briskly along, striking sparks from his four hooves in the grey dawn, and the young noble sat with his nose to the wind, as proud as Saint George.

All at once the peasant saw a bit of shining metal skip over the road. He ran to it, and picked up a nail which had just worked loose from the horse's shoe.

'Hey, sir! Your horse lost a nail!'

'A nail? stop for a nail?' thought the fine cavalier. 'It's not worth it. If I cut through the wood, soon I shall be at camp. I'll make him a present of it; at least he can't say that my present's not worth a nail.'

'Keep it, keep it, my good man,' he cried, waving his hand in farewell.

Clapping spurs to his horse, he took the short-cut, with no more thought of the nail.

As for the man, he thought of the old folks' proverb:

> Save a nail, bad or worse—
> Some day it may fill your purse.

He put the nail in his vest pocket, and went on.

He had not gone much farther when he saw a coach lying overturned against the embankment; one of its wheels had rolled some distance away.

The traveller was beside himself with impatience and vexation. In haste he came running up to the peasant.

'My good man, help me to repair the damage and I'll make it worth your while. Before this evening I must be twenty leagues from here!'

The peasant drew near. There was nothing broken; it was just that with the jolting of the road, where the army cannons had worn deep ruts in it, the cotter-pin that held the wheel had fallen out of the axle.

'If only you had a bit of iron to replace it, I'd gladly give you a golden louis,' said the traveller. 'Sometimes a bit of iron can be more precious than a bit of gold.'

The peasant took the nail out of his pocket. He helped the

traveller to put the wheel back in place, and made it fast with the nail, a good stout one with a solid head, forged by a blacksmith; to keep it from slipping, he wedged it neatly with a stone. There, the repairs were done, the coach back on its four wheels, and the golden louis in the peasant's hand. Had there been magic at work, he wondered.

But what gave him even more pleasure was to see the traveller, well content that he could now go on with his journey.

'If you are going to town, my good man, get in my coach and I'll take you there!'

Meanwhile the fine cavalier trotted along on his horse. But soon he had to change his speed. Once a nail is gone, soon the shoe works loose. The short-cut was more like the bed of a mountain stream than a true road. The poor beast stumbled among the stones and finally lost his shoe, so that the young blade was forced to jump down and go his way leading his horse by the bridle.

At last he came, swearing roundly, to a hamlet of three houses. He asked for the blacksmith. No blacksmith. All he could find was a hammer and tongs, and with these he could have put back the shoe himself in a makeshift way if only he had had the nail he lost on the road. But no nail! In this miserable village, not the smallest nail.

As they say, what you spurned with your foot yesterday, tomorrow you'd pick up with your teeth.

No nail. He must needs do without: bridle in hand, on he trudged in his heavy boots, cursing to pass the time, beside his limping horse. A cavalier does look a fool on foot.

Suddenly he found himself surrounded by a gang of ruffians—deserters, smugglers, brigands—who earned their living out in the woods. Eyes blazing, sword in hand, he threw himself upon them. Those in front drew back, but from the rear one of the rascals fetched him a blow in the legs with his staff that knocked him to the ground. They all fell upon him, beat him, stunned him, stripped him, and tied him to a tree, naked as a worm. There they left him, half fainting, in the depths of the forest.

Meanwhile the peasant, when the coach left him in town, set about buying provisions. A louis! It would have taken him two months, working by the day, to earn as much. In those days a man was paid ten pennies a day. He bought four round loaves, smoked bacon and sausages, dried pears and prunes, as a treat for his family, pickled herrings and a good-sized ham. For himself he was satisfied with the crust he had put in his sack that morning, a raw onion and some coarse salt. He ate, knife in hand, sitting on a curbstone, in a quiet street of convents and gardens, and after taking a brief nap, pillowed on his well-stuffed sack, at the foot of a wall, towards two o'clock, rested and well content, he set off, sack on his shoulder.

'Robbers? I'll take the short-cut through the woods, in spite of all the robbers. The main road is too far. And I'll keep my eyes peeled.'

He couldn't wait to reach home; he knew what joy he would bring. And so he went on his way, and thought of nothing else.

Deep in the thickest of the wood he pricked up his ears. In the distance he heard cries of distress.

He stopped and listened. Thinking of the brigands who were common in those parts, he hid his sack under the bushes and marked the spot, and then he walked boldly ahead, his knife open in his pocket, in the direction from whence he judged the cries to come.

In a few minutes he came up with those who were calling for help. He had made no mistake: the voices were those of a woman and children. He found a lady and a troop of boys and girls—seven or eight of them. Pale and forlorn, crying with hunger, they could hardly stand on their legs.

The lady, who was châtelaine of a neighbouring castle,

told him their story. Early the day before, they had set out on a walk from the castle, to see the budding green of the woods and lunch upon the grass. The children had picked wild daffodils to make chains and had run from bush to bush, listening to the birds. Led on by games of hide-and-seek, they wandered deeper into the forest. When they were no longer sure where they were, the north wind sprang up, and the fog closed in. She had grown uneasy, had tried to find a path home, and they had lost themselves in the mist.

Since the day before they had turned in circles in the depths of the woods, not daring at first to call, for fear of drawing evil men upon them. But at last in desperation they had been driven to cry out in spite of the risk, for they were half-dead with hunger and exhaustion.

'No fear of dying, madame,' said the peasant. 'In a quarter of an hour I'll have you back at the cross-roads.'

'Oh,' said the lady, 'but they could hardly walk two steps without falling with weakness. It's a whole day now and many hours besides since we have eaten or drunk.'

'If that's all, just wait,' said the peasant. 'I've enough with me to cure all your ills.'

In the old days it was truly a joy to render a service. If you knew that your neighbour was in trouble you could not rest. You rejoiced that you could help him; it was the deepest pleasure of your life—if your father and mother had trained you as they should.

He ran off, and came back in a minute, carrying his sack.

When the children saw the man unloading his provisions on the grass they could not believe their eyes. Hardly could they keep themselves from pouncing on the fresh bread, the pickled fish, bacon, sausage. Never in their lives had they made such a meal. The mother, laughing and crying, did her best to keep them within the bounds of good manners, and at the same time she kept on thanking the peasant, who was laughing as she did. To honest country-folk, there is no

pride or contentment like that of relieving those whom they find in distress. To be a Christian is just that: there is nothing finer on earth.

The children ate so ravenously that the lady blushed for them. They would have suffered from thirst if the peasant, who knew the woods, had not led them to a spring behind the pussy-willows.

> Ate well,
>   Drank deep—
> I pray the Lord
>   My soul to keep.

They felt all made new. The peasant was their guide to the cross-roads, and even to the edge of the woods and the castle, lest they should meet with any danger.

How they did thank him; his heart felt as light as air, but his sack too was lighter by far. The lady would have him accept her purse—through the meshes six or eight gold pieces could be seen—and, faith, with such a good grace that he had to take it.

He set off for home at a brisk pace, after nightfall, through the woods, all agog to be there with the gold in his pockets, when once again—could it be?—yes, he heard cries in the distance.

'Well, today the hue and cry's after me,' he said. 'Let's go and see.'

This time he kept on the look-out, and took all possible precautions, when through the branches he caught sight of a man tied to a tree, naked as a worm. And right away he recognized the young blade he had seen that morning.

He untied him, revived him, covered him with his rain-cape, and gave him something to eat.

The young noble soon came to his senses, sitting at the foot of the tree.

'After all, you know,' he said, smiling, 'it's for having turned up my nose at a nail that I am in such a fix.'

But the peasant, in haste to be at home, told him that he would take him to his house and shelter him for the night, and lend him his Sunday clothes for the morrow—even some money, so that he might get himself another horse.

An hour or so later the two men were sitting each at his own corner of the fire, in the old kitchen all blackened with wood-smoke. The children nestled close about them; they dared not open their mouths, only their eyes. The wind made a noise coming from the forest, the kettle purred, and the cat too, by the ashes. He who had lost the nail and he who had found it looked at each other smiling through the steam of the cabbage soup. Neither of them knew quite what to make of it all, after a day that was as strange as a dream.

All at once the young noble started up. 'Now I come to think of it,' he said, 'all my worldly goods are in danger of going to the devil and out to grass, like the nail, the shoe, and the horse. I need a man who is exact in all things to watch over my woods, my lands, my castle. You whom I know to be so wise, will you be my steward? In that way you will render me a far greater service than what you have just done for me.'

'What—I, sir, your steward?'

'Do say yes—you'll do me a great favour, and make your own fortune.'

Indeed, the dream went on, and the peasant agreed, as though he were part of it.

'So on that confounded nail,' he said to himself, 'was hung a whole new fortune. I do believe that never will I need to teach that proverb to the young ones. They'll remember for ever that if you

> Save a nail, bad or worse—
> Some day it may fill your purse.'

The Tale of Saint Peter's Chicken

ONCE UPON A TIME there was a man called Simon; he's the one they called Saint Peter later on.

On one of the days when Saint Peter still walked the earth he asked the good Lord, his Master, to have supper at his house; there was to be a roast chicken, to do honour to the guest. The good Lord promised that he would come.

Supper was all the good Lord could promise, and that a late one. During the day he had no time to himself. So much work on his hands: not only must he preach to the people, bring them back to the good life, but he must cure them of their ills, as he strove to cure them of evil. From the four corners of the land they brought him the lame, the deaf, and the blind. All the world came knocking at his door, until they stopped it up—think of it! A cure for you, and you; not a soul would give way to the next comer. To such a point that when they brought a paralytic on his litter, a man who must and would be cured, he was forced to make his way in from the roof; he had the tiles taken off and was lowered into the house like a bucket into a well. If this had taken place at Saint Peter's house—who knows?—Saint Peter would have had his tiles to put back again. And he would have grumbled about it, for he was a quick-tempered man. But he wouldn't have grumbled long; he was all good bread, was Saint Peter —good warm bread.

On the evening when he had invited his Master, he kept on grumbling and tugging at his beard because the Master did not come. 'Just see now how he lets himself be held up by all that riff-raff of out-of-lucks and good-for-nothings! There's a time for everything, and evening is supper-time. We were all given a belly. As for me, I can tell well enough that I have one and that it's empty. . . .'

It was true. All day long he had followed his master, with nothing to eat but a crust he had found in his pocket. Being a fisherman by trade, when night came he was as hungry as a hunter. And now the smell of the roast was strong in his nostrils. He sat there watching his chicken as it turned a golden brown on the spit; he basted it with the juice that ran down in the drippings-pan. . . . Soon the chicken would shrivel and char: what a pity! A chicken, now, that counts for something; it is more than just soup and fish. . . . As for fish, most likely Saint Peter had enough of them, casting his nets every day. . . . A dinner that boasts a chicken is a dinner you can take off your hat to!

And still the good Lord didn't come. No question about it, that chicken had to be taken off the spit, or it would be burnt to a cinder.

Saint Peter took it off, and put it on a platter. Without thinking, he licked his fingers. . . . But that was too much, that one little lick. Hungry as he was, he could bear it no longer.

With one twist of his hand, he tore off a leg, sank his teeth in it, and polished it off in three mouthfuls.

After that, well, Saint Peter looked a bit red in the face,

and tossed the bone under the table. Then he arranged the chicken as best he could—that is, he laid it on the platter on the side where the leg was lacking. 'There, there—you can hardly see it: no, you can't see it at all!'

No sooner had he finished putting all in order than his Master came at last.

They said the blessing. They sat down at table; they finished the soup, the cold beef with pickles, a few titbits; then came the turn of the chicken.

'I shall carve it,' said the good Lord. 'Peter, pass me the knife.'

'Lord,' said Saint Peter, perhaps a little redder than before, 'spare yourself the trouble. Here, I'll carve it.'

'Pass me the knife and fork.'

Saint Peter could but obey. . . .

The good Lord forked up the chicken, lifted it in the air, considered it. 'Just look, Peter—it has only one leg.'

'I see, Lord, but don't bother about that; the breed of hens hereabouts is like that. After supper I'll take you out to the hen-coop and you'll see for yourself.'

'Hens with one leg? I can't seem to remember that I ever created . . . But we'll look into that after supper.'

So after the cheese and the pears, Saint Peter, who knew what he was about, took his good Master out to the hen-coop. The hens were sleeping on their roosts, each one perched on one leg, her head under her wing.

'You see, Lord? Only one leg.'

The good Lord, as if to show his surprise and bewilderment, threw his arms wide and brought his hands together in a great clap.

All the hens woke up, cackled, and flew away. And there they all were, hens with two legs.

The good Lord turned to Saint Peter, and his look said, 'Well? Two, haven't they?'

But his eyes were laughing, and Saint Peter knew that he

was forgiven. Red, all red, redder than the cock's crest, he yet dared to laugh.

'Ho, Lord, who could argue with you? Miracles, you've got them at your finger-tips! When you wanted it, the hens had two legs. If you'd clapped your hands before the roast at table, away it would have flown with two legs, just like these!'

> The Cock has sung,
> The night is old,
> The day is young,
> The tale is told.

The Tale of the Singing Branch, the Bird of Truth, and the Water of Youth

ONCE UPON A TIME there was a king; he was getting on in years, but his blood was still young and his heart all fire. His chief wish was that all the people in his country might know happiness on earth. And a fine thing it is to wish for, when we let our deeds follow our wishes.

This king, then, set out to make a tour of his country, from house to house. He visited every one of them, and inquired as to how things went for all who lived there. And when he came across a young girl he asked her what she had seen in her dreams the night before. So much did he have every man's happiness at heart that he had forgotten to think of his own: he had never married. But he was very fond of talking with young girls.

When his trip was about over, before his return to the castle, he stopped in at the house of his nearest neighbour.

The man had three daughters, three fair lasses in bloom.

The king entered, greeted them, and addressed the eldest.

'What dream did you dream last night, damsel?'

'Oh, sire, I should not dare—it is hard to tell! . . . But if I must. . . . Sire, here is my dream: it was that I married your chief cook.'

'Very well, damsel, what you dreamed last night shall be fulfilled.'

He addressed the second. 'What dream did you dream last night, damsel?'

'Sire, it is very hard for me to tell you. Still, if I must, here it is, my dream: it was that I married your chief groom of the bed-chamber.

'Very well, damsel, what you dreamed last night shall be fulfilled.'

At last he turned to the youngest.

'Damsel, and you?'

The girl looked at him, and a blush rose to her cheeks that made her redder than a cherry, and her eyes shone like the star in the fountain. But not a word.

'And you, damsel?'

'Sire, to tell it is still harder for me.'

'Damsel, you must.'

Listen to her, the mad girl! What boldness! Still, that was her fate, and she was forced to confess the truth; simply, artlessly, with her heart in her voice, she told what was in her mind.

'Sire, my dream was that I married you, yourself.'

'Damsel, what you have dreamed this night shall be fulfilled.'

And with these words the king left.

To see the two sisters, snarling with envy, their blood aboil with malice, like cats in a fury! You would have thought them about to spring on their youngest sister and rend her with their claws. 'Look at her, will you? That doll-face, that pretty sweetheart! To think she dared! And the king let himself be caught by her wiles! The hussy, she need only throw herself at his head, and she will be Her Majesty the Queen! And we, her elder sisters, wife of her cook, wife of a valet! What shall we be? her servants?'

What they could not bear, those vixens, was the thought that if only the idea had come to them, the Queen's crown would have been theirs. No fear of their holding themselves cheap; to their minds they far outstripped their younger sister, both in beauty and in worth.

She, poor thing, before their fury, all she could do was to rub her eyes and cry. Red, and redder yet, like the wood strawberry, and fragrant as the berry, for when asp and salamander breathe out poison, it absorbs no venom from them. Would to heaven that the two sisters had thrown off their venom in their words and complaints. But it gathered in their hearts. From that hour they planned that one day they would wreak their vengeance. Powers of God, if people had only known. . . .

Shortly after, in the fair month of May, the three weddings were held. All went as the king had said: the two elder sisters became wives to the cook and the groom of the bedchamber; the youngest became queen.

Months passed. Then a great war broke out, and the king was forced to go. While he was away the queen gave birth to a son. Her two sisters were with her; they would not allow any but themselves to care for the child, nor take it to be baptized. Once back from the christening, they put the child in a basket, and the basket down at the end of the garden, on the river. Somewhere about the castle they had seen a little monkey—perhaps it was the king's whim to keep wild beasts in his castle. And the sisters took this bit of a monkey, and, instead of the little boy, they gave him to their sister.

Down a way, down a way, by a bend of the river, beside the water, was the garden of an old gardener and his old wife. They lived there together in a mean little house. The gardener had just transplanted his lettuce; it was time to water it. Down he went to the river-bank with his watering-pot. And there, under a willow-tree, he heard weeping. He looked about; in the midst of the mint and the wild iris, he found a basket, a tiny child.

Quickly he took it up, and brought it to the house.

'See here, good wife—guess what I've brought you!'

'And what are you bringing me, good man?'

'A new little boy! We've never had any: this one will be ours.'

In the meantime the king had come back from war. His wife had thought to show him their son, and it was the little monkey she showed him. The king was all amazement. . . .

And months went by. Another war must have broken out; however it was, the king went away again. And while he was far off, the queen had another son. And the two elder sisters, those vipers, played their evil trick again. But this time, instead of a monkey, it was a lion-cub.

And once more the basket came to land in front of the gardener's house. When he brought it to his wife, this time she threw her hands in the air.

'My good man! haven't we enough with one?'

'What could I do, good wife? I hadn't the heart to let him cry. The good Lord gave us another, we must take him.'

'Well, they can amuse each other.'

When the king came back, and when they showed him this lion-cub as his child, he wondered what sorcery was this. He swallowed three times before he could speak. In the end, he loved his wife so much that he told her he would let it go this once more, but that such a thing must not happen again!

A third war broke out. The king went off to it. Months passed, and there was born to the queen in her castle a pretty little girl. And, as before, the two sisters brought her to be christened in church. When they came back they gave the queen a crocodile.

Again the gardener heard a sound of weeping by the river, and in the reeds and the mint, under the willow, he found the new little girl.

'See here, good wife, what has come for us! The river has a grudge against us.'

'Already we have two boys, and you bring me another?'

'But this time it's a girl, good wife. She can help you in the house.'

The king came home. His wife, who thought to show him their daughter, brought forth this wild beast.

The king fell back several paces. Then, his hands before his eyes, he left the room. And he ordered that his wife be shut up in a tower.

The king thought of her a great deal. He saw her again as he had seen her that first morning, with the lovely fire of candour shining from her face. All rosy red, but looking him straight in the eyes, forced to tell him her dream, because that was her fate; simple as a clover-blossom, and smelling as sweet. And now it had all turned into these horrors. . . .

Perhaps he was too good, was the king. As they say,

> Simple and Saint go hand in hand,
> Far too good to walk the land.

It was not in him to conceive of baseness like that of his wife's two sisters.

Months went by, summers and winters. The king looked all of thirty years older.

In the meantime, the three children were growing up in the gardener's house. They had heard it said—perhaps by the beggars passing by, perhaps by the wind in the trees— that over the way where the sun rose there was a spring. By this spring could be found the singing branch, the bird who speaks truth, and the water that gives back youth.

To each one of them the gardener had given his own garden, and each one had a rose-bush growing there. The eldest boy wanted to go in search of the spring. 'I will bring you some of the water,' he told the gardener and his wife, who by now could barely walk, bent over their canes. They would not have him leave, but what he wanted that he would have.

He said to his brother, 'If you see my rose-bush withering it will be a sign I am in great peril.'

And he left, going straight before him, over where the sun rose.

He trudged along, along. By the side of a green meadow he met an old woman.

'Boy, where are you going?'

'I am looking for the singing branch, the bird that speaks truth, and the water that gives back youth.'

'So! Well, listen to me: when you are a bit farther along, put your two fingers in your ears; you will hear drums and sweet music, but watch yourself—don't move, don't listen: keep on your way!'.

Well and good: the boy paid heed to her, and did all that she had told him. He kept to the road and he stopped up his ears. But when he heard the music, like drums and flutes, violins and lutes, that rose with the force of a storm and swept all before it, ah, it was too beautiful; he could think of nothing else. He took out his fingers so as to hear the better, and down he fell, changed to stone.

Every morning and evening, when the dew fell, his brother went down to the garden and looked at the rose-bush. One day he saw the rose-bush turning yellow, and suddenly it died. Quickly he ran to find his sister, and his own healthy colour had left him.

'Watch over my rose-bush, watch over our parents. My brother is dead. I am leaving.'

Far away, on the road beside the green meadow, he met

the same old woman. 'Boy, where are you going?' The same words were spoken between them. Just as his brother had, he paid heed to the lesson. Going toward the spring, he stopped up his ears. But this grand music that came to him, so beautiful, he must and would hear. And down he fell, changed into stone.

That evening in the garden the young girl saw that his rose-bush had died. White of face, she ran to the house, and told them that she too must go now. A sad day that was for the gardener and his wife. They tried to hold her back with their old hands.

'No, no, don't you go, we have only you left. You see that your brothers are dead. Stay with us in the garden by the river! If you leave, you too you will not come back.'

'Yes, yes, I shall come back! I promise, it is a promise, but let me go.'

On the road, far away beside the green meadow, she met the old woman.

'Girl, where are you going?'

'I am looking for the singing branch, the bird of truth, and the water that gives back youth. And besides, I am looking for my brothers.'

'So! Well, listen. . . .'

Just as she had done with the boys, the old woman repeated her lesson. And all happened for the third time—she kept on her way, fingers in her ears, and heard the grand music.

But the young girl, when she heard this music that turned her head with enchantment, only walked the faster. On she walked, on and on, between the stones, the furze and briars, and at last she reached the spring. With the sickle she used for cutting reeds in the garden she cut the branch that overshadowed the spring, from which there flowed all this music that caught at your heart. It was like the sound of hautboys, fifes, and bombards, that flung you into a dance—you cut a thousand capers, you were leading the ball. She took the branch, with the bird perched upon it, and then she went to the spring, where she drew a pitcher of water. And she started for home, holding the pitcher in one hand and the branch in the other.

But what did she see? At the first drop that spilled from the pitcher the stone on which it fell turned into a boy. Thereafter, as she went, she let fall a drop of water on every stone. And each one turned into a boy or a girl.

In this way she reached a stone that became her elder brother, and one that became her younger brother. The elder on her right hand, the younger on her left, joyful in words and steps, they followed the green path that led back home.

There the old gardener, beside himself, was running as well as he could on his old legs, and crying to his old wife, 'The rose-bushes are green again! Our children are alive, good wife, and will come back to us!'

And just then, come they did. What a moment! Without delay, the girl took her pitcher and poured a drop on her father's forehead, on her mother's forehead. And the poor old couple, who were all dried up and wrinkled like the bark of a tree, found themselves fresher and greener than lettuce in season. Once again they were twenty years old. The children might have been fourteen or sixteen.

The girl set the branch and its bird on the mantel over the fireplace. The two brothers took their father's gun. They were so happy to be back that they must celebrate, along with their sister and their parents. On such a day they must have a piece of game for dinner, and they asked if they might go hunting.

Off they went to the woods, and right away they started up a deer; they flew in pursuit of it, from one mossy glade to another, among the chestnuts, beeches, and oaks. They bounded ahead in their ardour so far that, never noticing it, they crossed over from the forest into the king's park. And at the turning of a road, between the tall and venerable trees, suddenly they came upon the king.

Hunting on the king's land, in his park! And yet, if you can believe it, they were not so very frightened. Perhaps they simply thought, 'The good God has come to our aid so often that he will do it again.' Or perhaps not. They weren't afraid, that is all.

They looked at the king with frank, wide-open eyes, and the king kept looking at them, his eyes in theirs, while they, kneeling on one knee, cap in hand, answered his questions. They told him why they were hunting the deer, why they wanted a good dinner that day, and why they were holding a celebration.

Growing bolder, they told how a drop of water from the pitcher had given back youth to their parents, and they added that if the king would come to their house by the river, their sister would sprinkle on his head a few drops of the water.

And the king was stirred, and well pleased by what the two boys had told him. He felt like a dried-up rose-bush about to grow green once more. He left everything behind to follow the young huntsmen, to dine at the house of the gardener and his wife.

In the middle of dinner the bird began to sing upon the branch:

'King, here are your children three—
Monkey, lion, and crocodile, see!'

Three times he repeated the same thing. The king could not yet understand, but he wanted to understand. He forced the gardener and his wife to tell him where these children came from. Being afraid that they must give them up, they were not over anxious to comply. At last—it had to be wrung from them, question by question—they told how they had found the children: one, another, and still another

—each one in a basket on the river, among the reeds and the wild iris.

> 'King, here are your children three—
> Monkey, lion and crocodile, see!'

Again the bird sang upon the branch. The King asked to be shown the three baskets. Perhaps he recognized them as coming from his castle; in any case, he understood.

The girl took the pitcher, and poured out a trickle of water on the king's head. There he was, he too at the peak of twenty years; young again in face, body and bearing, just as he was young again in heart.

Straightway they must run, the children and he, with the pitcher, to deliver their mother, shut up in the tower. It was for him now to make her forget the misery of those years— she, so good, so pure, so true!

Afterwards the king gave his orders. His two sisters-in-law were to be seized and hung up like traitors from the castle walls, and all the world could come and spit in their faces. The people did not wait to be urged; no love was lost on them, those two.

As for the gardener and the gardener's wife, the king did not wish to separate them from their children. He sent for them to come and live in the castle. And since that day everybody has been happy, living with the water that gives back the freshness of youth, the bird who speaks truth, and the branch that sings great music.

The Tale of the
Too-Submissive Husband

ONCE UPON A TIME, in a certain village, there was a man of a genial and easy-going turn of mind. Too easy, for the girl he had married got the upper hand, and it was she that wore the breeches in the household.

Not satisfied with keeping his feet in the right path, she never lost a chance to assail his ears with home-truths. If he so much as trod on her foot when she was making ready for a holiday, all his past failings were trotted out. If he went to confession, there was no need of his searching his conscience; that had already been done. You might well say that he was ruled with a rod of iron. And all the work fell to the poor husband: the field-work, of course, and the household tasks besides.

On a farm iron tools are for the man, wooden tools for the woman. On his farm all the tools were for him—not only the spade and the shovel but also the rake. The man looks after the cows, the woman the goats, but on his farm he must play nurse to beef and billies alike. As month followed month, what didn't he have to do! Even fetching water at the fountain, even sweeping the house—even putting the wash to soak.

'It's my policy,' he said to the neighbours who were inclined to laugh at him. 'That way I save myself a lot of disputes. And he who laughs last . . .'

In the meantime he travelled a rocky road. Not a week that some new task did not fall to his share. It would soon be up to him to put fresh hay in the hens' nests, or hold up a straw to see which way the wind blew.

One evening when his wife had let fly because the milk had soured—all his fault, he should have scrubbed the crock with nettles—'Listen,' he said to her, as amiable as ever, 'why don't you make a list of all my jobs? Then I'll know which ones are mine, and I'll do them the best I can. Whatever isn't marked on the paper I won't worry about.'

So they arranged things on that footing. That very Sunday the schoolmaster came to draw up the list.

You may be sure that it was a long one. It took him all afternoon, and all the paper saved up to cover the jam pots. What a list, my friends! What a rosary of jobs! Well, paper is a good donkey, it will carry anything.

Three days after, as God willed it, something new came up. Easter was at hand, and the housewife was doing her spring washing. You know what a woman's temper is like on such days, and, as for that woman, you can imagine her.

She had just the weather she wanted, however—real wash-day weather, all wind and sun. Shadow and light flew by, turn by turn, white clouds skimming along on high, one hard on the tail of the other, as though their caravans were racing to see who would reach home first. But it was chilly, with a wind that cut you to the bone.

Have no fear for the housewife; she was well able to keep herself warm. As she hung her clothes on the lines, in the orchard, she kept on pitching into her man over some job which he was to have done that day and hadn't yet begun.

'And wasn't it set down on your paper? Just tell me that! Yes, tell me, you backslider, good for nothing but roistering, guffawing, drinking! Soft as soup, lazy as a slug! Ah, my poor mother, well she saw what would happen! Many's the time she told me . . .'

And so on. He had to follow her, carrying the load of wet clothes, and listen to her with both ears. When he went to fetch another load she raised her voice so that he shouldn't miss a word; and anyone going down the road a long way off could have heard her as well.

'So then, did the paper say that you were to shine my shoes, yes or no? And did I ever ask you anything more than what's written on the paper? Whatever's not written there, well and good, there's no need of your doing it. What's more, I'll thank you not to meddle with it, do you hear me, clumsy oaf?'

Just then, as though the wind wanted to stop her mouth, a tablecloth blew across her face. Blinded, she fell back a step or two, without seeing that she was near the willow-tree. Even had she seen it, she was too upset to remember that the cistern was gaping wide open, in the grass behind it.

All of a sudden, as she was struggling with the tablecloth, the ground slipped away from beneath her feet, and, waving her arms wildly, she tumbled into the water.

A tremendous splash and splattering, then her voice rang out: 'I'm drowning, help! Help, I'm drowning!'

No, that she wasn't, but the water came up to her chin, and it was far from warm. She caught hold of a willow-shoot, but it broke in her hands. She tried to pull herself out by a stone at the side, and the stone came loose. There was no way by which she could climb out. At last her husband, on his way back, heard her and came running.

'Hurry up—go get a ladder!'

The Tale of the Too-Submissive Husband

'Hey, but what were you saying just now? That I shouldn't meddle with anything but my own jobs? . . .'

'Pull me out of this hole!'

'. . . And that you'd thank me not to meddle with anything else? Did you say that or didn't you? This now, I don't really think it's down on the paper.'

'Quick, hurry, I'm chilled to the bone already!'

'Wait a minute, I've got the paper here. Just let me look—cook the pig's soup, give it to them with the whey . . . cut the grass for the rabbits. . . . No. . . . Here's the washing. . . . Light the fire, fetch the water, soak the wash, beat it, hang it to dry—all down there, but it's not written that I must pull you out of the cistern—no, that it isn't.'

'If you won't pull me out, I'll catch my death!'

'Wait now, while I look again—saw the wood, split it and bring in the firewood . . . mmm . . .' he wet his finger and turned the pages. 'Just wait . . . pull up the carrots in the garden, wash them, pick the soup greens, take out the honeycombs—it's all here; even pluck the chickens, but about the cistern and pulling you out of it, not a word. No, my poor dear, just look—it's not on the paper.'

'To the devil with your paper! Throw it away! Only pull me out of the water!'

'Aha, if you like. We'll throw the paper away and it's quite simple: you do the woman's jobs, like the nice little woman you know how to be, and we'll help each other as husband and wife should when they both behave themselves. On those grounds I'm willing.'

'Well then, all right, tear up the paper! But hurry up, dear man! I can see lizards all round me in the water. Oh, it's those beasts, even more than the water, that make my blood run cold!'

And so, like a good fellow, he hooked one of his arms round the willow, then stooped and stretched out the other to his little wife. He hauled her on to the grass, sopping wet, and he took her back to the house, all dripping. He blew on the coals, piled on armfuls of wood, and built up a good fire to dry her.

And it was the last time he lit it. From then on, in their home, the shoe was on the other foot. She had caught cold, and for a week she coughed away like Old Lady Whooping-Cough. But she behaved like a decent woman for the rest of her days. And that was well worth a cold in the head.

The Tale of the Two Ill-Married Men

ONCE UPON A TIME there was a poor man, and poorly enough he was married. His wife was one of those who make life hard for their husbands—you know, one of those wild cats. So much so that one evening, whether because of his marriage or from some other malady, he up and died.

Standing at the door of Paradise, he took off his hat and turned it about in his hands. 'I wasn't always as patient as I might have been,' he thought humbly, 'and every Sunday I felt I must take a few drinks and forget my wife—how do I know what all that will get me? Two or three hundred years of Purgatory, perhaps.' So he went on figuring, while Saint Peter was studying his great register.

'Good—it's a plain case,' said Saint Peter, suddenly closing his book. 'You can come in: you have earned your Paradise.'

'But,' said the man, unable to believe his ears, 'I slipped now and then, I know, and I was expecting a good stretch of Purgatory.'

'You were married to Zélie, weren't you? Come on in—you've had your purgatory on earth, right at home.'

At that another gentleman who had just arrived stepped up, touching his hat.

'Well, then,' said this fellow, 'in that case I can come in too, I am sure.'

'Oh, oh? Without Purgatory?'

'Ah, I've had it the same way, before my death.'

'Really?'

'And I even had it three times. I never knew the Zélie you spoke of, but, for my part, I married Julie—what a policeman!—then Gènie, then Mélie. Ah, it went from bad to worse.'

'So, after the first time, you remarried twice?'

'Yes, Julie, Gènie, Mélie. You can just see what I've been through!'

'What I can see is that there's no place here for you, my man!' And Saint Peter, with a wave of his arm, gave him the signal to clear out.

'Paradise is for the unfortunate, not the imbeciles!'

The Tale of Count Robert

ONCE UPON A TIME there was a young count, known as Count Robert.

On a Sunday in August, when he first awoke, he was seized with a desire to go hunting.

Hunting was his passion: to scour the fields on a valiant horse, at crack of dawn, with the dew still on the leaves, the white mist rising slowly, mingling with the shadowy branches of tree and bush. The birds cry out, and a bell rings in the distance. Far away on the crest of a hill a monastery and its chapel turn to rose in the light of dawn. The earth awakens: you are there, you are free, you may go where you like—stretching out before you is the whole long day of galloping through the leaves, of game, of good cheer, of the sound of the horn. . . .

It was a morning like that.

Count Robert sprang out on the stone staircase in front of the castle; he seized his horn and called his friends. They came running down, sniffing at the wind. Quickly he summoned them:

'To saddle, to saddle, and off to the hunt! For once you'll miss the mass!'

Swept them away, along the plain, from wood to wood, from clearing to clearing, in spite of the sun, which rose high and strong.

All about them was the smell of the hot grassy earth. Then the sky grew overcast; clouds came puffing up, and rode each other horseback, white, then grey, then black. Thunder rolled and growled in the distance, and then closer—it shattered and burst.

One after another his companions gave up the hunt. Seeing the storm over their heads, they tried to outstrip it; at full tilt they fled towards the castle.

But Count Robert was hot in pursuit of a deer, and on he went, despite the high wind that rose suddenly, blowing his hair in his eyes, and setting itself against him as he spurred his horse. On he rode through whirlwinds of dust and rain.

Suddenly there fell a formidable thunderbolt. An oak as big around as a millstone split in half, right in front of the horseman. His horse stumbled and shied, and then dashed away through the fields, in the midst of crashing thunderclaps and hammering rain.

The count sought in every direction for a refuge. The only roof he could see was that of a little church, standing far off and alone beneath some great trees.

In haste he made for it, tied his horse to the bars of the window, where there was shelter, and, putting his shoulder to the door, he entered.

He did not go far, feeling that he had been remiss in God's sight on this His day. All of a sudden he was overcome by lassitude; he found that he was too tired to take another step. Having crossed himself, he sat down on the flagstones, behind a pillar, in a dark corner.

The last light of day was slipping into the night. Leaning against the pillar, his shoulders to the wall, Count Robert sat

there half awake, half asleep, waiting for the end of the storm. The thunder moved away, but the rain kept beating on the roof and the surrounding trees in the midst of this solitude.

Count Robert had been resting there for some time when he saw a small door swing open—one he had not yet noticed, the door of a sacristy.

From behind it there came an old priest, tall and thin—as fleshless under his alb and his chasuble as though he were a skeleton. The priest advanced three paces, looked about him in the church, saw nobody, uttered a great sigh, and disappeared behind the door.

A moment afterwards he opened it again, came in, looked about him once more, gave the same sigh of disappointment, and went back.

'This must be some dead priest,' thought Count Robert, 'a poor soul out of purgatory. A priest who has promised to celebrate a mass, and who dies before he is able to do so, comes back to earth, they say, in order to discharge his duty. In the old days I have often served as altar-boy, and I should know how to serve at mass for him. If he comes back I must rise and offer myself.'

The priest came back. But Count Robert, as though he were tied limb to limb, found he could not stand up. And the same thing happened several times.

His heart was moved, however, and the more so because at each appearance the priest seemed more deeply troubled. Finally, at midnight, Count Robert called up all his resolution; he rose, came forth from his corner, and offered to serve at mass.

The old priest was overcome with joy and gratitude. For over a hundred years, he said, he had come back at night to this church without finding a soul to be his altar-boy. And now at last the mass could be said.

As soon as it was over, the priest turned to Count Robert.

'My blessing on you for the service you have rendered me! And what, my son, can I do for you?'

'Father,' the young count replied, 'I want for nothing. I have all I can desire at my castle—servants, clothes, food and drink, coffers full of money, more than I know what to do with. And dogs in the kennel, horses in the stable. . . . I want nothing but one favour.'

'And what is that, my son?'

'Father, that from this very hour I shall know the hour of my death. For if I am a Christian at heart I am hardly that in practice. Where religion is concerned I have not kept to the path, and I have strayed. And yet I should not wish to die without a repentant heart. Let me know in advance the hour of my departure, so that I may have time to be reconciled with Our Lord.'

'Very well, hear it, and never forget it, my son. You shall die in fifty years to the day, and at the hour of midnight.'

And the priest disappeared.

Fifty years! When Count Robert found himself alone he was glad at heart: half a century! How the days stretched before him, so far they seemed endless.

'I shall divide my time in half: yes, during twenty-five years I shall go on with the happy life I am leading. Then I shall have twenty-five years to live in retirement and make my peace with God.'

But the first twenty-five years went by like a day's hunting, a gallop on horseback. And God knows how the hours can fly, from chase to chase, revelry to revelry, hunt's end to hunt's end!

When the fifty years were half over, he had not the least desire, had Count Robert, to change his ways and his heart. He knew well enough that he had twenty-five years left. To repent for all of that time was really too much to ask.

'I'll give it another twelve years. In twelve years you can say a great many Our Fathers.'

And the time he had allowed himself went by like a flash of lightning. So many things to do, so many affairs, journeys, and celebrations! For his repentance surely three years would be enough.

And, heavens above, does one really need all that time to reflect on the good and evil he has done, and to do penance?

Then he gave himself a year.

Then a month. . . .

Then a week. . . .

And even the week, the last week, went by in the same sort of doings and diversions. 'Tomorrow, tomorrow, I must think of myself, of my destiny before God!'

And Count Robert found himself on the morning of the appointed day without even having made his last confession.

The day went by in haste and agitation. That evening, greatly troubled, Count Robert begged his mother to send for the priest, that a carriage might fetch him from the village.

'But you are not sick, my son—what are you dreaming of? Come and sit down to supper. Drink your wine, eat your meat.'

'No, I pray you! let someone go quickly and fetch the priest! I am going to die, mother, and the dead need no food.'

But his mother, his family, his servants paid no heed to him. They took his entreaties for day-dreams, his prayers for idle reveries.

And so he, with the face of a lost man, wandered from room to room of the castle. He saw himself as a man struggling in deep waters who knows that he is drowning and can find nothing on which to lay hold.

At last he did manage to dispatch a man to the village, and he threw himself into the great chair at the corner of the fireplace, to wait, hardly alive.

Time went on, on, on. How he suffered! Count Robert

rose, took a few steps, and then went back to his chair, trembling, unsteady, his mind distraught, his heart pounding. All he could think of was that it was now only a half-hour before midnight.

At last, at last, the valet came back from the village. But he did not bring the priest. They had sent for the priest to come to a dying man, and he was far away, in a distant village.

Count Robert tried to speak, and could only stammer; he was desperate. He sent the steward to some other village. But midnight was close at hand. A quarter of an hour, twelve minutes. Never could a priest be at the castle before midnight—it was too late. What would happen? what could he do to make time stand still? Nothing, nothing. His senses dazed and confused, his blood frozen, pulseless, voiceless, white, the count kept his eyes fixed on the clock. Only three minutes before midnight . . . only two minutes . . . the last minute. . . . The clock began to strike. . . .

At that, Count Robert woke up, just as midnight was striking from the church tower. He awoke still under the spell of his dream. He could not throw off that appalling moment, living over what he had just lived. He was borne down, as by a leaden weight, by the feeling that life had passed by, had taken him with it, and that now it was too late.

The storm was over. Outside was only a sound of dripping leaves. Count Robert was still in his dream. His thoughts ran as follows:

'I know myself—I do nothing by halves. If God gave me fifty years, I should live the whole of it in the same skin. Caring only for revelry and the pursuit of pleasure, all that separates me from God, swept away as one is at the hunt. Why, I should wait until the last minute to turn back. . . . There's no sense to it. From this hour I shall live a different life; my mind is made up.'

He took this resolution kneeling before the altar, and then he mounted his horse and rode back through the woods in the moonlight, deep in thought.

He took it and kept it; from that night on he lived the life of a good man, with a heart made new.

The Tale of Turn About is Fair Play

ONCE UPON A TIME there was a rich farmer. When he was in the prime of life and his father was already failing, it happened more than once that he treated the old man to some rough handling. For some piece of clumsiness or for-getfulness—say he'd broken a bowl, or let the fire go out —the man would even strike him down. Then, his anger rising, he would fall upon the old man with his fists and his feet, and finally, grasping his long white locks, he would drag him out of the house, on to the pavement of the courtyard.

But time passed, and his day came too—thirty or forty years later, as he had done to his father, so his son did to him. It seems to have been the rule of the house. . . . Like his father, he was thrown down on the flagstones and dragged out of the house by the hair. . . . Like his father, he could only cry out and endure.

At night, unable to sleep, wretched man, he brooded over

his lot, and at least he realized that it had been meted out to him by the just judgment of God.

One day the son had felled him at his feet, battered him with blows of his fists, and, seizing him by the hair, this son dragged him in a fury across the stones of the courtyard. But that day the madman did not stop there; he went through the gate, and dragged his father over the pebbles, along the road under the walnut trees.

It was then that the poor wretch started up in revolt.

'Ha, no, my son, you go too far!' he cried. 'I never dragged my father by his hair beyond the courtyard gate!'

The Tale of the Grain of Wheat

ONCE UPON A TIME there was a man who went about begging, sack on his shoulder. They called him Jean-Jean. He made his rounds from farm to farm; taking crusts of bread from his sack, he asked for a bowl of soup to sop them in, and then asked for more crusts and a bit of cheese besides, when he saw that people were disposed to give.

But there came a day when he had no luck with his begging. As soon as the farmers saw him come, 'Shut the door! Loose the dog!' For two long days Jean-Jean had gone about with an empty belly.

He had such a sorry look, dragging his sabots along, with his sack flat on his back, that an old woman who saw him pass took pity on him. She was twirling her spindle in the middle of the pasture, and she made her way down the road.

'Poor man, listen here!'

He came to her, and in the palm of his hand she put a grain of wheat.

'See that you don't lose this grain.

> Knock on any door you will,
> Warm shall be your welcome still.'

'Many thanks, good woman, many thanks.'

He slipped the grain in his vest pocket, and away he went over stock and stone, heather and waste land. From time to time he put his finger on the grain in his pocket, to make sure it was still there. Night fell, and far away he saw a house on the edge of a wood; he went up to it and knocked at the door.

'Good evening, mistress and all the company. Have you a place for me to sleep, I and my grain of wheat?'

They made him welcome. With a good will they made room for him round the fireplace, they gave him soup; the mistress prepared him a bed in the hay-loft. No doubt of it, the grain of wheat had a power.

Before going to bed, as was the custom, he gave the master his matches and knife. He also gave him the grain of wheat, charging him to take the greatest care of it until morning, for he would ask for it back. Then he went to the hay-loft and spent the night in the hay.

The master put the grain on the table, and, my word, he left it there and forgot it. We all have so much on our minds.

The next morning the mistress was the first to rise. She lit the fire, opened the door, went to see the cows in the stable. Through the open door came a white hen; she knew there would be crumbs for her to pick. She turned her head to right and left, and hopped up on the table. There was the grain of wheat. Cric! A tap of the beak and it was gone: the grain was swallowed and gone.

Poor Jean-Jean! He came in just in time to see it happen. He tried to throw himself upon the hen, but it was too late.

'My grain of wheat! oh, misery me! I held it dearer than the apple of my eye! Bad luck indeed your hen has brought me!'

The master was a decent man, and when he saw Jean-Jean mourning and lamenting he proposed to make good his loss. The mistress came with her hands full of wheat.

'But that's not the same wheat my good woman gave me! I must and I will have my own grain of wheat!'

'Poor man, what can I do? It's still in the hen—well, take the hen!'

So Jean-Jean went off on his rounds with the hen under his arm. At least, he thought, he could sell this fat hen in the next town. But night fell before he reached it, and once more he must take shelter at a farm.

'Good evening, mistress and all the company. May I sleep here, I and my fat hen?'

'Come in, poor man. We'll put your hen in the hen-coop and you on the straw.'

He slept like a king, but the white hen did not find it as easy. The farmyard hens went for her with their beaks, so hard that in the end, bleeding and half-dead, she fell into the pig's trough, and the greedy beast ate her up.

In the morning Jean-Jean found nothing left but her feathers.

'My hen! my poor hen! No, no, I don't want another hen, nor two hens. If the porker ate her, it's the porker who ought to pay for her.'

And moans, groans, and complaints, until the master threw up his hands.

'The pig did the harm; take the pig—what more can I say?'

The pig was not a great huge one, and Jean-Jean put him into his sack and then off on his rounds. But with such a burden, he didn't travel far that day, and it wasn't late when he asked for lodging at a prosperous farm.

'Good evening, good folk. Would you let me sleep here, I and my pig?'

'That we will, my good man. Put your pig in the barn, and we'll fix you up a corner by the farm-hand's room.'

But that night the pig felt a bit strange, and wanted to make the round of his new lodging. He went too near the red cow, and the red cow let fly with her hind leg and knocked the life out of him.

Next day, when Jean-Jean saw that, heaven help us! You wouldn't have wanted to be near him.

'You were in charge of my pig—give him back to me! No, no, not a fatter pig. It's my own pig I want, or else the cow that killed him.'

And he'd do this, he'd say that, he'd point out the other! Until in the end they had to hand over the cow.

He made them give him a rope, tied it to her horns, and led her away. 'I'll make some pennies, I'll make some pennies!' He saw himself walking down the road to fortune —he need only go straight ahead.

That evening he came to another farm.

'Evening, good folks! Have you a corner for my cow and a pallet for me?'

Yes, yes, they'd put the cow in the barn and find him a bed.

Next morning he asked for his cow.

'Ah!' said the mistress, 'deary me, poor beast, last night she got loose, worse luck; she went behind our horse, who's ticklish, and the horse kicked out and knocked her dead.'

'So ho, you needn't think you'll get away with that! My cow, I want my cow! . . . No no, not a finer cow. I must have my cow, or the horse that killed her.'

And he'd do this, he'd say that, he'd point out the other! He yelled and carried on so that, being decent folk, they ended by giving him the horse. And he took the bridle too.

So off he went on his horse, riding with his hand on his hip, proud as a louse on a priest's shoulder. 'I'll be getting rich! I'll be getting rich!'

From a grain of wheat to a horse! Fortune was on his side, and all went merrily. By tomorrow why shouldn't he have a house, a wife inside it, a good piece of land round it? Sitting on his mount, enthroned on his sack folded twice for a saddle, he cast his eyes over fields and meadows as though he were already lord of the land.

The Tale of the Grain of Wheat

That evening he came to a large inn: 'Lodging for Man and Beast.' On the doorstep, catching a breath of air, was a pretty girl, a tidy wench, as we say, and also a big crooked dog, lamed by a wagon that rolled over her back. He stopped, got down, and threw the reins proudly to the girl.

'Room for me and my horse?'

'At your service, sir.'

They gave him supper and a good bed, and that night he slept in clover. The next morning he came down and gave orders for his horse to be saddled and for a glass for himself.

'Ah, sir, there's been a misfortune. Our daughter took your horse to drink at the pond; it was dark, the beast slipped on the bank. . . . In short, the beast was drowned. All we can do is to give you another, a better one. . . .'

And he'd do this, he'd say that, he'd point out the other! A regular witches' sabbath. Jean-Jean carried on, yelled his head off. He knew his rights, and he demanded either his horse or the girl who had let him drown.

'No, no, none of that! No better horse for me: what I want, good people, is my own horse, the same one!'

So long did he cry that he must and would have the girl or he'd have the law on them, that in the end the inn-keeper said, 'Well, here, take her and be quiet! I'll give you what you want. But my wife could never bear to see you lead her off. Just hand me your sack—I'll pop her inside, and you'll take her away.'

And in a minute he brought him back the sack, all tied up, heavy and wriggling. Jean-Jean hoisted it on his back as best he could, and took to the road.

The sack weighed heavy on the hill, but he trudged along with a light heart. He said to himself, 'I've got the girl! Tomorrow I'll come back and get the inn!' And hoisting the sack on his back, he started off again, singing:

> 'To the greenwood I will go,
> And there I'll kiss my darling. . . .'

So he went on and on, climbing up to the wood. When he came to a shady spot he unloaded the sack, took out his knife, and cut the cord.

The sack fell open. With a bound out leaped the crooked dog, bigger than a mastiff. Growling, she flew at Jean-Jean's nose, bit it off with a snap of her jaws, and ran away.

Jean-Jean, knocked sprawling, picked himself up, bleeding and howling, and ran after the dog, as if he wanted his missing morsel back again.

> 'Stop, stop! the crooked cur
> Took my nose away with her!'

But the dog galloped along, her hind-quarters switching from right to left, and Jean-Jean galloped after her, still bawling, the blood streaming like a fountain from what was left of his nose. This devil's crew tore down the hill, faster than a hurricane, while Jean-Jean, all disfigured as he was, cried as loud as he could:

> 'Grain of wheat to fat hen,
> Fat hen to boar pig,
> Boar pig to red cow,
> Red cow to white horse,
> White horse to pretty maid,
> Pretty maid to crooked cur
> Who took my nose away with her!'

But all they could do for Jean-Jean was to make him a wooden nose. What's more, if I know this story, it's because it was my great-uncle Robert, the town sabot-maker, who carved the nose like a sabot, out of the red wood of a briar stump.

The Tale of the Two Neighbours

ONCE UPON A TIME, in a village, there were two women who were neighbours. One of them was rich and stingy and hard of heart; as for the other, her means were small but her heart was like a piece of gold.

On a certain evening a beggar passed that way. He knocked at the door of the rich wife, and she—well, she shut it in his face, without so much as a 'God help you, poor man!'

So he knocked at the door of the other, who had little enough for herself; none the less, she set before him a bowl of buttermilk and a thick slice of brown bread. She threw wood on the fire to warm him, and told him that she would fix him a bed out in the hay.

'Many thanks for your good heart, good woman. I'll be on my way before nightfall, thank you kindly. But tell me, what would you like to have in your house that would make life easier for you?'

'Why, I don't find life hard. I have about all I want. Ought I to ask for more?'

'Good woman, you shall have your reward.

What you do, the day begun,
Shall you do till set of sun.'

He spoke, and he vanished into the dark of the road.

Next morning, when she awoke, the good woman took no thought at all of the beggar and his words. It came to her mind to measure a piece of linen she had been saving, to see if she had enough to make a bonnet for Sundays.

She held up the cloth, stretching it from finger-tip to arm-pit, as women do when they measure goods. But what an odd thing! There she was, measuring, measuring, while the linen in her hands kept on doubling, doubling—rolling itself up in lengths of a hundred ells, and after one length, another, and still another. And so it went on all day.

By evening the house was full to the ceiling with rolls of linen, and if you said that the smallest one was worth fifty crowns you wouldn't be a penny out of the way.

The good woman had all the linen she could want until the end of her days, and enough besides to sell and to give away.

In a village everyone lives in his neighbour's pocket. By nightfall there wasn't a household that didn't know what had happened, and all the women had come to see the lengths of linen fallen from heaven by the gift of the poor beggar.

And the rich wife! What a rage she was in, to have lost such a windfall. The envy in her heart came near drying her up like a stick of wood.

Three days later, before her anger had left her, when evening came she heard a rap at the door.

She went to open. It was the beggar, passing by again.

'Come in, my poor man, my good man! Since that other evening I've been so sorry! My head was turning with all I had to do—the washing not finished, a hen who goes to lay in a neighbour's barn—everything to vex me. . . .

The Tale of the Two Neighbours

And I did so want to welcome you!'

A flood of words, and a hurry-scurry to receive the poor man. She put the skillet on the fire, broke eggs against the edge of the table, cut a fine big slice of ham, and, while waiting for the supper, she poured the beggar a brimming cup of white wine. But all this was to be tit for tat. Here is wine, omelet, and ham: where's my reward? You might well say, was her heart in it?

Supper once eaten, she offered the poor man the warmest room, the feather bed.

'Woman,' said the beggar, 'you shall have it, your reward.

> What you do, the day begun,
> You shall do till set of sun.'

Aha, when she heard that, how glad she was! And she meant to waste no time measuring cloth, flour, or the like. Counting gold pieces, that was more like it. What a fountain that would be—a flood of gold pieces!

For it was a sure thing; the beggar had proved his powers. The wife could see it as already hers. She saw herself lady of the castle, dipping three spoonfuls of cream into her soup every morning — she could have done this already, but wouldn't—wearing her Sunday dress week-days, and enthroning herself in the first row at church. All the women of the village would burst with envy.

You could hardly say that she slept that night. One eye stayed open, at least, to watch the window—would it never grow light?—waiting for day to break.

At last the cock crowed.

Then the sun rose.

Aha! now she must snatch up her purse.

She saw herself shaking out the first golden louis, when, as luck would have it, a flea bit her on the ear. Willy-nilly, she raised her hand: she had to scratch herself and try to catch the flea.

Straightway the beggar's words took effect:

> What you do, the day begun,
> You shall do till set of sun.

At the touch of her fingers there swarmed, there sprang, not golden louis, but fleas . . . but fleas! Flea after flea, to bite her, once and again, to hop on to the bed, the bread-chest, the dresser, the clock—all over the house, until the house could hold no more of them. The neighbours came running to see this wonder. The woman, as her fate decreed, was all day long after her fleas. But when night came, with her house a-swarm and herself besieged, she could stand it no longer. She took to the door, and took to her heels. And since that moment she has never been seen again.

The Tale of the Boat that Sailed on Land

ONCE UPON A TIME there was the king of a great kingdom, who had a daughter ready to be married.

This girl was inclined to be proud, but she was very beautiful for all that. The king was in no hurry to find her a husband. He liked to have her near him, wide-awake as a goldfinch, straight as a reed, and sunny as an Easter day. He didn't want to give her away to any boy, even though it was a king's son. Besides, he thought, where could he find a prince worthy of her? 'My daughter, the daughter of the king of a great kingdom!'

Only, there came a time when queen and scullery-maid, Prime Minister and shoemaker, castle-folk and townsfolk alike, never missed a chance to remind the king that he had only this one girl, and that she must be married. If no prince could be found to suit him, let it be to some clever boy, who would some day be equal to taking the kingdom in hand.

'That's what you want, then?' cried the king, one morning when his Prime Minister had been harping on the need for a husband, 'a clever fellow you must have? So be it—off we go! On the stroke of noon, have the trumpets sound it abroad that I shall give my daughter to the man who can take wood from my forest and make a boat that sails on land as well as on sea. Yes, to the man who comes to ask for her riding on that very boat!'

He thought to himself, 'Before any man born of woman shall bring me such a boat, that can sail the fields as well as the waves, plenty of water will have run under the bridge. And those old crows will stop splitting my head with their shall I, will I, must I marry off my fair maid!'

In the same kingdom, not far from the castle, there were two brothers, two country youths. The elder was so clever that his fingers could make anything he wanted; as they say, he could have made eyes for a cat.

Only, he knew that he was clever, and rather too well. To have faith in yourself is a good thing, but it is better yet not to carry that faith too far. The boy said to himself, 'If there is anybody who can make a boat that sails on land and on sea, who could that be but myself? I shall make their boat and then make them give me this daughter in marriage— and if I can't, nobody can!'

He provided himself with axe and saw and hatchet: in his sack he put hammer, chisel, and gouges, and off he went with a light step towards the king's forest.

Along the way, by the hill of the Fairy Beeches, he met an old woman, one of those who gather dead branches, deep in the woods. She wished him good day.

'Good day to you, young carpenter! You are up early this morning?'

Courtesy required that he stop and answer the old chatter-box, but he kept on his way, full of his own importance, as though already he held the world at the tip of a pitchfork. He answered her greeting with a curt nod of his head.

'Where are you off to work, so brisk?'

'That's my business.'

'And what are you planning to do with all those tools?'

'Make ninepins.'

'Ninepins they'll be, young carpenter, ninepins they'll be!'

And so it befell that once he had begun his task, in the king's wood, no matter what he cut down, shaped, and built, it all turned into ninepins. He began again, took elm and ash, rather than beechwood, and the same thing happened— ninepins, nothing but ninepins.

His blood was up, and he flew in a rage. 'Name of a name of a great sacred blue cow!' He caught up chisels and gouges, axe and hammer, and sent them flying into the underbush. But he only made himself double trouble—that of throwing them, and that of picking them up.

In the evening he came home, looking like a man whose prize team of oxen has been dehorned.

'I ran across one of those old women with the evil eye,' he said to his brother, without waiting to be questioned. 'But, in any case, what a fool I was to fall for that nonsense! A boat that sails on land as well as on sea! You could sail, and sink too, before you'd finish that job! . . . The king was only making fun of us all.'

'Are you sure?' said the younger brother. 'Time is father of miracles, they say: you should have gone on.'

'Well, go on yourself!' retorted the other, angry again. 'Just let's see you go to the king's wood tomorrow and try the job for yourself!'

The younger brother did not answer. It hadn't entered his head to try, but he would not refuse. He could only hope that the way would be shown him.

Next morning he took the sack of tools, and, humming a song, set out for the woods. By the hill of the Fairy Beeches he met the old woman. She came hobbling up to him, bent over, one hand on her hip, like one of those old women who go after dead wood.

177

'Good day to you, young carpenter!'

'And to you, good woman!'

'Where are you off to work, so brisk?'

'My brother sent me to the king's wood, to have a try at making the boat the king wants. I don't know if I can do it, but sometimes ideas come as you work.'

'A good thought, young carpenter. And why shouldn't you make that boat? Just try it!'

'Oh, if trying's enough, I'll try!'

'When it's done, climb into it and go to find the king. On your way you'll meet six dragoons. Bring them along with you. Might come a time when you'll have need of them.'

The younger brother bowed and thanked her, and took his leave. In the king's wood he shed his coat and fell to chopping trees.

And behold! all the wood that he chopped took its own place; one branch became the axle, another the rudder—some planks became the gunwale, others the poop. The pieces dovetailed themselves together in order, the hull took shape and rose before him. At length the boat which the king had dreamed of with no thought that it could ever be had grown beneath his fingers, as a pine-cone grows upon a tree—but a good deal faster.

The carpenter sang and the work did itself. At noon the boat was done, fresh from the workman's hand, whole and perfect, and even carved with fair ornaments.

The younger brother climbed inside it, to see what would happen. The boat started rolling down to the pond, set off on the water, and then back to land—and it sailed as well on land as on water!

When he saw that, the younger brother steered his boat along the road that led to the king's castle. And, with neither horses nor mules to pull it, this chariot-boat darted along so fast over rivers and ponds, waste land and moors that tall poplars were swept backwards, and the whole country seemed to fly by.

The younger brother, then, went along with his hair flying in the wind. Many in his place would have thought themselves the darling of fortune, but not he.

On the way he met a man, a sort of dragoon, with a belly like a huge goatskin of wine, stretched out upon it at the river's edge. When anyone wanted to cross the river, he sucked it at one gulp into his great paunch, so that the passer-by might cross over dry-shod.

'Ho, you, what are you doing there?'

'Emptying the river.'

'Have you no other trade?'

'None at all, and it earns me my living.'

'Climb into my boat, and I'll take you to the king's castle.'

Some way farther on he met another man, a sort of dragoon also, with a mouth like an oven door; he was gnawing at the mountain, with a great crunching of teeth.

'Ho, you, what are you doing there?'

'Gnawing the mountain.'

'Have you no other trade?'

'None at all, and it earns me my living.'

'Climb into my boat, and I'll take you to the king's castle.'

Some way farther on what did he see but another dragoon, with a backside as round as the full moon. This one was blowing a great blast at nine windmills up on the hill.

'Ho, you, what are you doing?'

'I'm puffing out wind!'

'Have you no other trade?'

'None at all, and it earns me my living.'

So the younger brother took this ruffian as the third on his rolling boat.

Then there was a fourth dragoon, with ears like cabbage-leaves; stretched out on his side, cheek to the ground, he was listening to the dandelions grow on the other side of the earth.

He too, this Quick-Ears, had only this one trade, and earned his living by it. The younger brother took him, too, in the boat—and off for the king's castle!

And then? Well, a fifth ruffian, with arms like fishing-poles, who could bring down larks by throwing stones at them for more than a hundred leagues about him. He too had no other trade but that, and it earned him his living. Climb on, climb on! So he too got into the boat which went as well on land as on sea.

And then? Well, a sixth and last, with legs like long poles, and glad of it, because he could outrun hares, catch them on the run, or pass them. He had no other trade, and this one earned him his living. 'Come on, you too, climb on board!' So off they all went together, to find the king.

In a very short time they reached the castle. All those inside it came running out, crying their astonishment. They swarmed about, unable to believe their eyes, unable to take them off the boat—from the greasy kitchen-boy and the old darning-woman, needle in hand, to the king, the queen, and the princess.

The king stood there staring, his crown crooked on his head, all in a flurry and a pother. He had given his word; he had even had it proclaimed with a flourish of trumpets. Could he refuse his daughter to this young fellow who came to ask for her in all good faith, standing on a boat that went by land as well as by sea, just as he had said?

'Yes,' he said, stroking his beard, 'the boat can pass for the one I had in mind. My word is given, the word of a king; I do not take it back. All that is left to arrange, before the wedding, is one small matter. Oh, almost nothing. In my cellars the wine has turned a bit sour with the heat. It would be an unchristian act to throw it out, and an unseemly one to serve it at the wedding of my daughter. Before night either you or one of your men must drink up all the wine in my cellar so that tomorrow we may fill the barrels with a new vintage!'

The younger brother listened to the king respectfully, cap in hand. When the king had done he made a sign to Drink-the-River.

The dragoon fell to work as though he hadn't drunk a drop for nine hundred years. And it didn't take long, though these were the king's cellars, with leagues of galleries, rows upon rows of hogsheads and barrels. Down went all the wine; even the barrels would have gone, if that had been asked for.

The king, all amazed, pinched his nose. 'Just one more small matter,' he said, 'next to nothing. He who drinks the sea can eat the fishes. There's the bread, now. It would not be seemly to serve stale bread at the wedding of my daughter. So, before nightfall, either you or one of your men must eat up all the bread there is in my kitchens.'

The younger brother made a sign to Gnaw-the-Mountain. The other set to work, and it didn't take long! In less than a minute all the loaves, long or round, had disappeared. All the baskets would have gone too, if that had been asked for. Even the stones of the oven.

The king knit his brows. 'Well,' he said, 'there's still another matter to settle before the wedding. Oh, hardly any-thing. I find my castle much too dark, facing toward the north. You, or another of your men, must turn it around towards the south, by blowing on it.'

The younger brother, cap in hand, made a sign to Puff-Windmills. The dragoon raised a great wind that buf-feted against one of the wings of the castle. . . . And the castle spun around three times like a teetotum. . . .

The king knit his brows still harder.

'I will go now,' he said, 'and climb to the highest chamber

of my tallest tower. I shall whisper to my daughter, with my mouth up against her ear, about something she must go and fetch before her wedding. Either you or one of your men must overhear the secret, and repeat it to me just as I have said it.'

A wink of the eye to Quick-Ears. And Quick-Ears had only to stretch out his ear to overhear the king's secret. The king had told his daughter to go to his treasure tower, at the top of the mountain, and fetch her wedding finery.

The damsel mounted upon a fine white horse, and set off at a gallop. Her head was in a whirl; she had not yet made up her mind just what she thought of this marriage.

The king took his pipe out of his pocket, filled it, lit it, and smoked it. Everyone else stood about in silence, respectfully, waiting for the princess's return. As for the boy, he began to wonder if the wedding bells would really ring, not yet daring to believe himself so close to heaven. So the time passed.

'Heavens above!' said the king. 'I forgot to give my daughter the key of the tower! And now it will be too late. There can be no wedding. . . . Unless,' he went on, tapping his pipe against his finger-nail, 'you, or one of your men, on foot, should catch up to her horse, and get back here as soon as she.'

Quickly the boy made a sign with his chin to Long-Legs, who set off with great strides, and in no time at all he had caught up to the king's daughter, given her the key, and reached the tower with her. She took all her finery, turned the horse's head about, and gave him a touch of the whip.

As you may see, she was a proud girl, with a taste for promptness and secrecy, like her father. Marry a village boy —after all, why not? But she hadn't yet deigned to take a look at the younger brother.

And so she urged on the white horse, and he went like the wind.

As for Long-Legs, much he cared; he had to hold back, so as not to overshoot her.

When the king's daughter saw that, she thought of a trick. She pretended to be tired, stopped her horse, sat down in a green meadow under the shade of an acacia tree, and said she was going to take a nap. Evening drew on. Long-Legs, the messenger, sat down beside her, and grew sleepy too. His head fell upon his chest, and off he went to the land of dreams.

He had taken the precaution of sitting on the edge of her skirt. But the sly girl softly, softly drew away her robe, leaped in the saddle, walked her horse on the turf, and then, leaving Long-Legs asleep by the roadside, she spurred her horse and galloped home at top speed.

Meanwhile, the younger brother's mind was on the girl. He wanted her, this girl who hadn't even looked at him! He was on the watch, and when he saw neither the girl nor Long-Legs, he was beside himself.

'Ho, Quick-Ears, listen a bit, tell me what is happening!'

'This is what is happening,' said Quick-Ears, 'your messenger is snoring. He's fallen asleep somewhere. And the king's daughter is on her way alone.'

'Ho, you! Stone-thrower, quickly, quickly! Wake him up with a little stone, right on the end of his nose!'

Long-Legs leaped up, awakened by the pebble.

The princess was nearly home now, in a cloud of dust. They could see her coming, at the last bend of the road—the white horse going like a hurricane, his four hooves striking fire from the road.

But Long-Legs too came in sight, hardly touching the ground: you saw him in flashes, like lightning. The horse galloped headlong: he flew. He passed it by three lengths, and slowed up, to arrive at the same moment as the princess, before the king and them all.

And this time the king was obliged to give the young man his daughter for wife.

The evening of the wedding they set off, the boy, his bride, and his men, and the bride told Quick-Ears that he must stay close by them.

As for the boat that went on land as well as on sea, they had not had the king's leave to take it. Moreover, he, the bridegroom, before they left, had caught several black looks aimed at them. It seemed to him that something was cooking for them that wouldn't set well on their stomachs.

But he could think only of the king's daughter. Since she had sworn faith to him, nothing evil could befall them. At last the girl had looked at him, from her white horse, when she rode back to the castle, and she had seen what stuff he was made of, this boy who had done the impossible for her, over and over again, in spite of all that the king had contrived to keep them apart, he and she. A country boy he was indeed, but his eyes did not speak like one. He had surmounted all his trials and acted none the prouder for it; he did not brag nor lord it about. Cap in hand, straight as a poplar, his face clear and smiling, he told it in all simplicity that it was the fairy from the hill of the Fairy Beeches who had done it all.

The princess was no fool. And so, the very evening of the wedding, as she knew the ways of the court, she asked Quick-Ears what the courtiers were saying there.

'My lady, everyone has made such a pother about this wedding to the king your father that he is furious. He has just given orders—three thousand men have been sent to pursue you: they are to seize your husband and bring you back to the castle.'

'Think of that, now! A pretty state of affairs! A good thing to be warned in time!'

The little party drew itself up in battle array. Quick-Ears chose a height as a listening-post. From time to time he gave the young couple his report on all that was going on at court and in the army camp. Long-Legs was messenger, and flew from one to the other, carrying orders. Stone-thrower, attacking with a shower of stones, began the battle.

Gnaw-the-Mountain gnawed through a mountain to let the younger brother and the princess pass through. Drink-the-River drained a river so that they might walk across dry-shod, but when the king's troop came up, he disgorged it in its bed, and they were halted by the stream.

And, to end it all, Puff-Windmills was waiting for them. His wind bombarded them all. Bang—bang; boom boom baroom! Plumes and hats, capes and baldricks, flew in every direction before the blasts; carts, teams, cannons, squadrons, battalions and all, whirled about like chaff. In less than two minutes the field of battle had been swept clean.

By honest trickery the younger son had made it all march quick-step on the fields and on the waves, before the wedding and after the wedding. The king was very much vexed. And then, well, his rage died down.

He said to himself that if his son-in-law had the fairies on his side, then he had better make up with the fellow. He let them come back to court. Once on a friendly footing, everything rolled along on an even keel, in youth and old age, in good weather and bad, exactly as did the famous boat that went as well on land as on sea.

The Tale of the Young Rake

ONCE UPON A TIME, in a city of Brittany, there was a young man of good family, whose name is not given, so that no slur will be cast on his kinsfolk. But he belonged to the quality, and was well known in that region.

He took life as a carnival, and his last prank was worse than a folly. Hear his story, young people of today, draw near and hear what befell him, the evening of Mardi Gras, in the town of Rennes, in Brittany.

To enhance their masquerade, he, and a few companions as dissolute as he was, had the mad idea of parading through the streets with one of their number dressed as a spectre. And so they went to the graveyard to look for the head of a dead man.

Inside the skull they put a lit candle, or perhaps a lantern. The young rake fixed it on his head—yes, the death's-head on his own head—and wrapped himself in a white sheet. In this wise he seemed to be a giant spectre in whom there burned the fires of hell. His comrades helped him to array himself, and then, in a band, they ran about the streets, as wild as bells jangling in the night.

The Tale of the Young Rake

Women put their hands over their faces, children screamed, and everyone ran away. Panic followed in their wake as, dizzy with wine and bravado, they made the town ring with oaths, bawdy jokes, and blasphemy, and followed their every fancy in order to cap the carnival.

At last they settled down in some inn to a grand debauch. They laid waste flesh, fish, and fowl; pipes and pots on the table, they guzzled till they could hold no more. Their heads were reeling with the smoke, the noise, the bumpers. This was high living!

They broke up at last, towards midnight, laughing, singing, and drunk enough, poor wretches, to overflow the bridges.

'Before we take leave of one another,' the young rake managed to say, 'we have a duty to fulfil, out of common courtesy. Our dry-bones may be feeling upset over losing his head. We owe it to ourselves to give it back to him.'

And so, singing and laughing louder than ever, they all went back to the charnel-house and placed the head upon the pile of bones. The young rake took off his hat to it.

'Our dear departed, you were most obliging to do us this favour. In return for your services, may I ask you to dine with me, tomorrow evening, at this same hour?'

The next evening, Ash Wednesday, it may well be that the boy was slow in coming to himself. That evening was he even able to remember what he had said and done the night of Mardi Gras?

He dined as usual, and, when night fell, he went to bed.

But at the appointed hour, that is, at midnight, there was a knock at the door.

At the first knock the servant came to open it. When she had done so, she fell down in a swoon.

Another knock at the door. At the second knock the mother came to open, and she too swooned away.

At the third knock the boy came himself.

187

On the threshold stood a spectre. By the stains of wine and candle-grease upon it the young rake knew the death's-head he had worn for Mardi Gras.

He cried out with an oath; staggering back two paces, he fell against the wall. The spectre, leaning forward, spoke with him face to face.

'If tonight you do not care to dine, let us pray God, let us go to our beds. In a week you shall be lying with me, side by side. Out of respect, or else bravado, you brought back my head to the graveyard, and so I bring you a week's delay. Now, look to your conscience: in a week, Wednesday for Wednesday, midnight for midnight, your hour will come!'

The Tale of the Man
with the Fiery Rose

ONCE UPON A TIME there were three girls, who were going out for the evening one Sunday. Word had gone round the week before that there would be a large gathering from all the villages roundabout that evening, and that a ball would be held. It was half an hour's walk, but little they cared how far, when it was for a ball! These three girls, I am bound to say, were no better than they should be; all their thoughts were of dancing and gadding about.

As they went their way at the first cross-roads they met a young pedlar. Tall, shapely, and of easy bearing, dressed in black, with a rose in his mouth. He carried a small pedlar's pack over his shoulder.

'Greetings, good evening to you, young ladies. And where are you off to so fast?'

'We are going out to dance at a neighbour's.'

'Will you give me leave to follow you?'

'Follow us? Why not? The roads are free.'

But it was said with no unkindly look.

'May I take part in the dance?'

'The people who are giving the ball are well off; there'll be no lack of straw or hay to sit down on.'

The pedlar followed the three girls. And he gave each one of them a ribbon, a red ribbon; he tied it about their wrists. Some say that he tied it as though in sport, without a word, and that they did not even notice it.

They went their way, laughing and talking, over the meadows, the rocks, and through the woods. All four arrived together at the house where the ball was to be held. Many young folk were already there, ready to start; they were playing a country-dance.

Rose in his mouth, the man stopped at the door. One of the girls, seeing that he was not following them, came back.

'You're not coming in?'

'The master must give me leave.'

'Oh, they don't stand on ceremony here.'

'I must have leave: I must have a word from the master.'

The girl ran to find the master.

'There's a young man, a wayfarer, a pedlar—we met him just outside the village. . . .'

'Well, let him come in. Oho, the house is big enough—he won't be likely to fill it.'

'He came along with us—he'd like to take part in the dancing, but he's particular in his ways: he'll only come in if you'll invite him yourself.'

The master went to the door.

'Come on, young man, in with you! Prayers are for priests and putting on airs for tailors. The ball is for one and all. If you want me to tell you to come in, I do so tell you!'

'Since you wish it, I come in by your leave. And in return, if ever you come to my house, you shall be well received.'

'That's good, young man, and we'll have a drink together —we'll empty the bottle. Perhaps your cellar is better than mine.'

'Agreed, and I'll keep your place.'

'And where is your house, young man?'

'The road is an easy one, and you need only follow it.'

'Tomorrow you'll show us. This evening let's laugh and sing. Here are the girls: see that they dance, now!'

The young man bowed to the company, and offered his thanks and his compliments. He was easy to listen to, that fellow, just as he was good to look at.

At first he sat down on his pack by the corner of the fireplace. But very soon he stood up, and took one of the girls with the red ribbon at her wrist.

And then! . . .

It seemed to the others that they had never seen dancing before. Supple, light as a cat. Tired? never. Out of breath? not once. When the girl's head spun so fast that she could stand no longer, she stopped and asked for mercy—and he took the second, then the third of those who wore the red ribbon at their wrist.

And then, one after the other, he made them all leap in the air and spin in his arms, and he spun the faster, laughing, and his laugh was like the sound when you tear a piece of cloth, a laugh to curdle your blood. He held them with his glittering eyes. Without knowing what ailed them they began to sweat and tremble.

And still they must dance, and dance, higher and faster, though they were foaming like spent horses. Someone held them by their hands, their waist, their neck, drove them, flung them hither and thither—someone who was either laughing or grinding his teeth, and both were terrible. They spun about, their hair clung to their wet cheeks, their eyes stood out of their heads, faster and still faster, turning like a wheel, while he, with great bounds, leaped until his head touched the ceiling. 'The house is large enough, he won't fill it,' had said the master. But, flashing everywhere at once, he seemed to fill it with ease.

A little boy in one of the coffer-beds along the wall cried out to his mother.

'Mother! look at that gentleman. I see a rose of fire in his mouth!'

'You're only half awake, child—you're still dreaming!'

'Oh, no, mother—look, look! his feet too—they strike sparks. He's all red, as if he were made of hot coals and flame. . . .'

'You're dreaming, my poor child, and what you say is folly. . . .'

But, being the mother and mistress of the house, she looked closer, and she ran and spoke to the master.

'Oh, who is it we have let into our house?'

Fear laid hold on them all. Girls and boys, feeling that there was something beyond nature about this ball, began stealing towards the door. The host went up to the dancer and said:

'Let's do as they do, and go to bed. Come, young man, the ball is over: it's time to go now.'

But go he did not; he sat down deliberately on the hearth-stones beside the kettle.

'See here—who are you?'

'Does that concern you?'

'I'm in my own house; it does concern me.'

'I won't tell you.'

'If you are the devil himself, I tell you to get out.'

'I shan't go.'

'I'm master here, not you.'

'You gave me leave to enter.'

'If I gave you leave to enter, now I give you orders to go.'

'Who's to make me? You'll see what I do with them!'

He stamped, and a piece of the floor split off as though cleft with an axe.

They sent for the parish priest. But the priest was old and lame: he was loath to climb so far at dead of night, over roads full of stones, ruts, and running water that wound between banks and hedges.

'You go up,' he said to his curate, 'and see what is happening.'

The curate went off through the black night; he climbed the mountain for a good hour, at the risk of breaking his leg, and finally arrived.

He came in, and saw the man as they were all beginning to see him—black, with split hooves, horned brow, and a look that struck terror.

'So it's you? And what are you doing here?'

'Let's say I'm amusing myself.'

'Enough of your games—come on, off with you.'

'Who'll put me out? Do you think you can do it, half-pint?'

The devil meant that the curate was worth only half the priest, the pastor of the parish.

'I'm not afraid of you—do your worst.'

The curate opened his book, said his prayers, and scattered holy water. Nothing: the other laughed at him.

'You're too young. Go back to the presbytery, fetch the priest.'

Going back to town did not take long, but the old lame priest took well over an hour, pulled and pushed along by the light of a lantern, to reach that far-off village hidden in the woods.

Before opening the door he went down on his knees on the stone threshold and fell to praying. Then he went in.

'What are you doing here?'

'I'm amusing myself.'

'You won't amuse yourself with me. Get ready to leave.'

'Go take a walk.'

'In the name of God!'

The devil turned and leaped upon him, to bear him to the ground.

The priest had only just time to cross himself. But at the sign of the cross, as though by a blow of the fist in his stomach, the devil was flung back three feet in the room, legs and arms in the air. He swore, spat, stormed—his eyes shot fire.

The priest took holy water and a sprig of boxwood. When a drop of holy water fell upon the devil, it was like the touch of red-hot iron. He leaped three feet in the air and howled.

The priest raised his hand. 'I ordered you to leave.'

'It is for you to leave—a ball is no place for you. Where there is dancing that is my place.'

'Get out!'

'The master of the house gave me his leave—no taking it back!'

'He received you by charity. Any more reasons?'

'First, what I gave must be given back.'

The priest turned to the girls. 'What did he give you?'

'A ribbon.'

'Give it back to him.'

They gave it back, trembling, but where the ribbon had been there was a mark like a burn.

'They wear my mark: I shall take them along with me.'

'You ask too much. Begone.'

'If I leave, let those in my path beware!'

'You'll not begin your tricks until you are out of my parish!'

'I am leaving: you will see my traces. Shall it be by fire, by wind, or by water?'

'You will leave by wind.'

The priest marked out a path from which the demon must not deviate. Everything was agreed upon.

Suddenly the wind rose. In the village the tiles were blown from the housetops, even the stones that weighted them down, and in the woods the pines were scattered like a row of matches, one tumbled upon the other. In his path it looked like no earthly country.

In the house the people had fallen on their knees, trembling. Heads bowed, they repeated the Lord's Prayer. It might have been the end of the world. Never again did they say the Lord's Prayer as they did that night.

And then?

The priest told them in his next sermon that there must be no more of these gatherings that broke up so late. He forbade the village girls to attend them.

Do you think the girls were ready to mend their ways?

Next Sunday, the very next Sunday, they set out once more, gadding about the roads, bent on dances that lasted until midnight.

Only there was someone waiting for his revenge.

On a night when one of the three girls was on her way home from a ball he was waiting for her at the cross-roads, there where he had met them the first time. He asked her if he might walk along with her. And it was enough that he was a handsome fellow—she said yes, mad creature that she was. The demon and she went off together in the night. Lucky the girl who can keep her head and her virtue!

They came to a fork in the road; the right-hand fork climbed up to the village where the girl lived, the left-hand went down towards the mountain stream. The demon seized her by the wrist, at the place where his mark still showed red. In spite of her cries, he pulled her along the downward road, towards the deep roaring waters.

'Help! help!'

Little use to call for help when it is hard on midnight! People are all asleep, their curtains drawn, their shutters closed, snug in their beds.... Only one old woman heard her, in the nearest house, the last one of the village. And she was bedridden.

Dragging the girl along, the demon stripped her as he went. . . . He could not have done so, they say, if only she had worn something that had been blessed—a rosary, a

195

sacred medal. . . . She had nothing but the mark of the ribbon. . . . Her apron flew here on the grass, her dress ten paces farther along, on the gorse, and her skirt twenty paces farther, on the stony bank. When she found herself in the stream, dragged there like a wounded beast, she had nothing left but her shift.

In the middle of the stream was a flat rock, and on it the demon strangled her. The water runs rusty by there, as though it was stained with blood. You can still see the marks, graven upon the stone—those of her head, her body, her heels. On each side of her marks there are the marks left by the demon, and they are those of hooves, those of a beast.

The Tale of the Lady
and the Hind

ONCE UPON A TIME there was a lady, fairer than daylight.
She was a child of noble lords and the wife of a noble lord.
From her childhood on her thoughts had been only for the
works of God. She cared less for games and dances by
torchlight in the hall than for prayer in solitude at some
chapel in the woods.

When she was eighteen she took for husband a young
count of the highest lineage. And even then, in the joy of
youth and love, she sought for seclusion. Her longing for
prayer and meditation was so great that at times she would
have left her castle for a hermit's hut lost in the forest.

Her husband, touched by her piety, let her live as she
pleased. He had seen that she was beautiful and good, and
he had given her his heart with all his faith. He knew that
she could do nothing that did not shine with God's light.

In the spring a great war broke out. Wars there have
always been, because men have not learned to be children of
God, and until they learn, wars there will be. The count

took the field with his knights. A great hardship it was for him to leave his beloved wife, and as great a hardship for her to see him leave—he who was still her dear love. And it was the harder for both as they were awaiting a child to be born by winter-time.

However, part they must, and it was in her mind that he went forth into danger, and in his that she would be alone in the castle to meet any misfortune that might befall her.

He could do no better than entrust her to his steward, commending her over and over to his good care.

By ill luck he put all his trust in this red-faced fellow, whose eyes held a cold glint of envy and treachery.

As soon as the master had gone the steward began laying his snares, trying to entrap the lady. At first he thought that he could win her easily by smiles and false words, dropped as though by chance. Being all light, she did as does the sun which shines upon the mud and is still the sun. Being all mud, he could not believe that she was what she seemed. He thought her childish, simple, even silly. So he set out to open her eyes, and bend her to his will.

She drove him from her presence. And he, in a rage, swore vengeance.

First, because he craved it, and afterwards because he feared that if he did not kill the lady she would reveal his betrayal to the count. Goaded by rage and fear, he laid an atrocious plot. He saw to everything, he thought of everything. Seizing a moment when the distraught lady sought for solitude and peace in her oratory, he slipped into her room, and hid beneath the bed the jerkin of a kitchen-boy, a poor deaf-mute.

In the middle of the night he came and made a great outcry before the door, and pretended to pursue someone he had seen fleeing down the stone corridors. When the valets came running at his cries, he declared to them that, on making his rounds, for he had had his suspicions, he had seen the deaf-mute, half-naked, escaping from the lady's chamber.

With the devil's own boldness he made his charge against her, as if, against his own will, he needs must champion and avenge his master. Then, still consumed by the zeal of a faithful servant, he ordered that a search be made, and saw to it that the jerkin was found beneath her bed.

Straightway this monster sent two valets to kill the poor weakling, well knowing that he was innocent. The lady, by his order, was hauled to the dungeon, and he cast her himself into the darkest and smallest of the cells.

The following morning he went to see her, and let her understand that he could yet cleanse her of this stain, or, on the other hand, he could plunge her deeper into dishonour, even have her put to death. She must listen to reason, he told her, and see things as they were—fixing her with his little eyes sunk in grease.

The lady looked at him without a word. She trusted in her own innocence. Whatever this traitor or any man might do to her, all that concerned her was to keep her feet on her own path, which led to God.

Autumn came, winter drew near. In her lightless cell, between its walls of dripping stone, where she slept upon straw, she gave birth to a little boy. A lovely child, the son of her lord, the companion of her days, when she had lived in the light of the sun. But he was far off at the wars.

In its time war ended, peace came again. The steward, learning that the count was on his way home, went half-way to meet him. They met in a city, when the count was in the midst of his knights. Before them the steward told his story of what had happened that night at the castle; he accused the lady of having betrayed their master, and called forth as witnesses the valets, whom he had brought with him.

The count could have been no more stricken if a thunderbolt had fallen at his feet. He suffered death and passion;

henceforth, could he believe in any woman, anybody, anything? So many witnesses, the facts so plain. He listened without finding a word to say. His mind wandered, he was beside himself.

All that was clear to him was that to doubt what had been told him as a matter proven, and to insist on further inquiry, would be, in the eyes of his knights, an unworthy weakness.

And then he had come from the war. He had seen all the excesses, the horrors that flesh and blood are capable of. He no longer knew if there could be human beings who do not yield to them, men who control themselves, women who remain pure. And yet the idea that it was his beloved who had done evil consumed him like fire.

He spoke, then, only to say that his wife and child must be put to the sword without delay. When he should reach the castle three days from then he must find it rid of their presence. There must be nothing to remind him that they had ever lived or died, and their names must never be spoken again.

The traitor went back in haste, with no trace of pity in his heart for the innocent lady, the innocent child. He would even have her stripped before him of her raiment and given the rags of a beggar-woman. Then he gave her into the hands of two henchmen, the coarsest and roughest that he could find in the castle, and charged these two brutes that they must knife both the lady and her suckling child in the heart of the woods.

'Go now! Bring me back her heart and her tongue!'

Her child on her arm, the lady followed her two executioners. As she was leaving her cell her little greyhound came running up to her, happy at seeing her again. He lay flat at her feet, beating the earth with his tail, and then jumped around her. Wagging his tail and barking for joy, the dog followed her on her way.

'So,' said the countess to herself, 'he who owed me his

help and trust condemns me and sends me to my death. On all the earth there is no love for me, save in the heart of this poor beast. . . .'

She went on to her death, between the two henchmen, who led her into the woods, from thicket to thicket. Deeper they went and deeper yet, as if they could find no place far enough, or lonely enough.

At first there was space between the trees through which the wind and sun might pass. But finally they came to a sunless spot in a dense thicket, overhung with branches. And there they stopped.

'Men who lead me to my death, will you grant me this grace? Kill me first: then I shall not see you cut the throat of my little child before I die.'

Then one of the henchmen, seeing her as defenceless as a lamb, could not keep from sighing.

'What shall we do? I have kept on and on: I had not the heart to stop.'

'Our orders were,' said the other, 'that you must die.'

'Lady,' went on the first, 'the steward has condemned you, and yet I do not see how I can do this.'

'What shall we do,' said the other, 'if we do not obey him?'

'Well,' said the first, 'for myself, I know what could be done. We kill the dog, and we bring back his heart and his tongue. Lady, you were always good to us: how can we do evil to you? I had rather not think of what my eyes saw, but I know that never have you done evil.'

'At least,' said the other, 'keep yourself well hid: stay in the depths of the woods, and never let the steward, nor anyone else, see you again.'

So they killed the dog, and by his death the poor greyhound served his mistress for the last time.

They went then to wait upon the steward, in the lower hall of the castle. Without a word, they held out their bloody hands: one of them opened his fist and showed him a heart and tongue, and the steward took them to be those of the lady. He said nothing of the child, knowing that he could not live without his mother.

The thought never entered his mind that the henchmen might be deceiving him—as if he alone were capable of deceit.

So there she was, the unhappy lady, abandoned in the forest, without bread, lodging, fire, or light. Betrayed, rejected by her dear companion and by all those who called her their lady, and with no other company than that of her child. But God's care was over her.

In the heart of the forest, where tall young oaks grew thickly, she found a glade full of ash, beech, and wild pear-trees. A sandy path led to a cool ferny spot where a spring welled forth. Behind some hazel bushes was a grotto hollowed in the rock, with a pine tree overshadowing the door.

'So often have I longed for solitude: this time I have found it,' she said, between smiles and tears. And in spite of all she was happy to have saved her child from death.

She took shelter from rain in the grotto, and there she lived like a hermit of the woods, digging for roots, gathering fruit from the bushes. But hermits cultivate the ground, they build a fire in their lodging—when night comes they light a small lamp. They have flint, a hoe, a knife, a sack, a bowl. . . . While she, the countess, who had seen valets and waiting-maids striving to anticipate the least of her wishes, she had nothing. What a life of penance, and for a crime she had not committed!

'But there are others who sin,' she thought. 'I shall do penance for them, as well as for my poor sins. The Son of God was without sin, and he had to endure while they spat upon him and beat him with whips; he bore the thorns, the nails, and death upon the cross. Why should I fare better than he, the Innocent?'

The Tale of the Lady and the Hind

Thus she kept in her heart the peace of God, even in misery and injustice.

She wasted away and lost her milk; there was nothing left in her breast with which to feed her child. 'My God, you who would be called Our Father, will you let my child die?'

And behold, a hind pursued by the wolf who had killed her fawn came and took refuge with the lady. And the hind who had lost her fawn suckled the child.

The wild beasts of the woods were company for the lady and her little one; they played before them and made them smile. The wild sow and her little pigs came, all in a row, nose to tail—then the deer, the badger, the weasel, and the fox with his sharp nose, waving his tawny brush. They trotted across the greensward disporting themselves, caressing and being caressed. Without fear, far from all those humans who are no more than appetites, flesh and blood, ruse and murder, near this mother and baby, it was as though they discovered at last the kingdom of the secret Age of Innocence, under God's sun. There at the lady's feet the fox played with the young rabbit, the wild cat with the robin. Birds came to visit her; snipe and partridge, hawk and woodpecker lit on her hands; with full throats they sang upon the bough, as though their hearts overflowed. Before this innocent who suffered without complaint, and sought but friendship, the innocence of the earthly Paradise was born again, in the light from above.

And so this went on, far from the world, until there came a certain day.

All this time the lord count stayed alone, crushed by his sorrow, in the depths of his castle. To divert him from his thoughts the steward devised hunts and feasts, but he was in no mood for such pleasures. Unceasingly his soul turned to the lady he had lost. 'How could such things have been?' he asked himself. 'There was a sort of light about her. . . . I would have sworn she could not lie. . . . But no, I was foolish and credulous. It is the men who laugh with half-shut eyes who see straight. . . . And still, could it be?'

Out hunting, he sought to withdraw from the others, to ponder these things in his mind, for it seemed to him that in what had been told him there was something he had missed. The thought haunted him that in the light of justice he had not made all clear, and it was like a knife in his side.

One evening when he was hunting in the forest and had drawn apart as was his wont, he caught sight of a hind beneath the branches, and he set out in pursuit of her with his dogs.

The hind could have escaped them, since the dogs were already tired, but, strange to say, she made no attempt to leave them behind. She led them through an oak thicket to a far and lonely spot, dense with trees and thorn-bushes. Between the tall grasses she took the sandy path to the spring and the grotto. Thus she led the hunter to the child, to whom she then gave suck.

In the dark of the cave he saw first the child, and then the woman who held him on her knees. She was fair as daylight, and her long hair fell all about her.

'Are you a living creature?' he asked, so amazed that he could hardly speak. 'Who are you? What are you doing here, in this dark spot?'

'I am a countess,' she replied, 'but my husband, who had entrusted me to a traitor, was willing to believe that I had done evil, and he sent me away.'

All trembling, the count asked her for her story. Did she even know it? Ah, but she had only to speak: there was no need of explanations or proofs. All her words shone with the clarity of truth. He knew her now, she whom a church sacrament had made his life's companion for this world and the next, she whom he had sworn to aid and protect; he knelt before her, weeping, and begged her to forgive him.

'What, is it you, lady, you for whom I weep? You who

were, who are, all my life! How can I lead you to forget my folly? Ha, for long now I have smelt foul play, and have cursed it. . . . By God's grace I have found you again, alive, with this fair child!'

And, because God willed it, at this moment, with shouting and horns barking and hallooing, the rest of the hunt came up with them. The huntsmen, struck dumb with amazement, gathered about the count, and recognized the countess and her child. They found themselves of a sudden faced with a prodigy: the stag that they were following fled them no more; he lay down at the lady's feet. The pack of hounds made no more noise; peacefully they lay down too, and the men, unaware of what they did, fell down on their knees. Men, dogs, and wild beasts, touched with a joy, a grace they had never known, rested there together, as though bathed with the peace of Paradise.

When the lady left, her child on her arm, close to her lord count, then, fearing neither dogs nor huntsmen, all the beasts of the wood, all the birds of the air, came to salute her, and weep over her departure. The hind even followed her far out of the forest, as far as the castle. Wheeling above her head, the birds lamented with small plaintive cries, while the rude huntsmen felt their hearts melt within them by the grace of love.

They do not suffer in vain, those whose hearts are pure. Their suffering wipes out sorrow and evil; it makes the world clean, and gives it back into the hands of God.

The two henchmen who had turned away from murder were each rewarded by the count with a farm and flocks. And the lady would have saved the life of the traitor, but here the knights would not listen to her. They condemned him to death, and it was a hard death.

For this is a world of blood.

The lady was not made for the world. She lived only a few months, once she was back from her solitude. Her husband, seeing her waste away, surrounded her with care, but all in vain. She faded, she languished away. She raised her white hand from the bed to say farewell to her lord.

'I must leave you, but our child stays with you. Whenever you look at him, my sweet companion in the forest, you will think of me, your companion of yesterday and of for ever—of me, and of faith and remembrance. In Our Father's house some day we three shall meet again.'

Long did they mourn her, her husband and child, all those of the castle and countryside. It was said that at the hour when she gave up the ghost a ray of light came down from the skies, as though to show her the path to heaven. All the people saw this marvel: it lasted a whole night. From towns and farms all over the countryside, people came flocking to the castle of the saintly lady. They followed her body to the graveyard, where it was laid away in the earth.

And the hind of the woods; she, too, followed them. She stretched herself out on the grave and lay there; she would not touch anything brought her, she would not eat nor drink, and on the third day she died.

The Tale of the Ogre and his Farmer

ONCE UPON A TIME there was an ogre who had a castle at the top of a mountain. He lived there with his ogress and their servant, and his farmer lived at the foot of the hill, in a bit of a house that had barely room for himself, his wife, and their twelve children.

One year, by ill luck, the new wheat froze in May and came to nothing. You may well believe that life was hard that year. There were only a few sacks of grain left in the loft, and the farmer put off as long as he could the moment when he must share them with his master.

So well did he put it off, so many good reasons and fine stories did he find, and his dozen children had such a good appetite, that a day came when the sacks were empty. Even by scratching in all the corners a rat couldn't have found a bite for himself.

The farmer wasn't too easy in his mind. He knew that he was in for a bad time when the ogre came down from the castle to claim his due.

'Listen, wife,' he said one evening, 'it won't be long now till he comes. See to it that you keep a soup-kettle of boiling water on the fire. And you,' he said to his children, 'try to have eyes in the back of your heads and all round them: watch the castle. As soon as one of you catches sight of the ogre, let him run and tell me.'

Three days later the farmer was digging turnips in his patch of a garden: it was evening. All of a sudden he heard his eldest: 'There's the ogre!'

And the child came running like a rabbit.

The farmer left his turnips and darted into the house. He caught up the soup-kettle, in which luckily the water was boiling briskly, and set it down three paces from the threshold, between the pine-tree and the spring. Then he took down an old whip hanging by the stable door and began to run about the kettle, whipping it with all his might.

Just then the ogre came up, crimson with anger.

'My wheat! I want my wheat! This time, farmer, no more dilly-dallying.'

But the farmer was so busy that he saw nothing, heard nothing. The ogre had to catch him by the neck and shake him like a plum-tree.

'Oh, sir, beg pardon, excuse me! I was only just whipping my kettle, so the water would boil for soup.'

'What nonsense is this? Do you cook soup by setting it on the grass?'

'Yes, sir—the kettle came to me from my poor great-aunt. You see, it's a fairy kettle, and so is the whip.'

'And you make the water boil by whipping the kettle?'

'Yes indeed, sir—just look.'

The farmer took off the lid: the water was still dancing inside, steaming like a horse at the top of a hill.

'My word, that's true enough!' said the ogre. 'You whip it and it boils? I wouldn't mind having that. Why, I'd like to show it to my wife. Just hand me over your kettle.'

'Alas, sir, and what would we do without it? Think of the wood we'll need. . . . Your servant drives my children away if they go in the forest to pick up dead wood.'

'Pick up all the wood you need. And I'll let you off that wheat you owe me.'

'No, no, sir; I'm going for your sacks right now. Our kettle! my great-aunt's kettle!'

'Listen, now: I'll let you off all the wheat, and give you a pig besides. My servant will bring it down in a minute.'

'Before night, sir?'

'In a minute, I tell you!'

The ogre was dying of envy to have the kettle, if only to make his ogress's eyes stand out, and he put his hand on it in such haste that he burned his fingers. He caught up the whip too, and lugged it all back to the castle at a good round pace.

Next day the farmer was shaking in his breeches. Well he knew that if the kettle wasn't on the boil the ogre's wrath would be.

And there was no counting on the ogress to calm him. The ogre's first wife had not been too mean, no more than was reasonable for an ogress. By constant walloping he had sent her into the next world. Afterwards he had taken a second wife, as mean as a hornet, and always ready to go him one better in sound and fury.

'My word,' said the farmer to himself, 'we may as well eat the pig right away—we'll be that much to the good. Afterwards, let come what may!'

They had killed the pig, and had just finished making blood-sausage, when the eldest child, perched up in the pine-tree at the corner of the house, came tumbling down, crying, 'The ogre, the ogre! Here he comes!'

'Quick, children, put the meat in the cupboard! Clear away, hide everything, and step lively. You, wife, come here, hand me the sausage. Sausage, knife—hurry up!'

He wrapped three lengths of blood-sausage round his

wife's throat like a necktie, and tucked her kerchief over it; hardly had he finished when he heard the ogre, running as though he were after his dinner.

'Ha, you wretch!' and the ogre fell into the house like a thunderbolt. 'You'd put my arm out of joint, would you, whipping your kettle? Come along, now—it's not the kettle, it's your carcase that'll be dancing!'

The farmer was berating his wife so hotly that he seemed not to have heard a word his master was saying. 'No bread!' he cried, dancing up and down. 'No soup, nothing to eat in the house! We can count ourselves lucky that she's left us four walls! Oh, oh, hussy that you are! I don't know what stops me from knocking you flat!'

He gnashed his teeth and foamed in a frenzy; he boiled up and down like milk on the stove. In a transport, he caught up a knife lying on the table, and struck such a blow at his wife's throat that the blood spurted out like a fountain, and the poor woman fell flat on her back.

It was so sudden that the ogre could not move hand or foot.

The farmer had only pierced the blood-sausage, you understand, but all the blood had poured out, and it ran in a red stream to the door. Lying there as stiff as a log of wood, the farmer's wife looked already cold in death.

'Ha, bandit!' the ogre said at last, 'that was ill done— you've cut your wife's throat.'

'Yes, sir, I cut her throat. It's not the first time, and it won't be the last.'

Quite unconcerned, the farmer went to the fireplace, picked up the bellows, and blew two or three gentle puffs into the corpse's nose, saying over his shoulder:

'There, sir, you'll see her come to. You won't find bellows like that on every tree; they came to me from my great-uncle, and they can bring the dead to life.'

The ogre's eyes were as round as full moons. In good

truth he saw the farmer's wife draw a sigh, blink her eyes, sit up, stand up, and right away she fell to storming at her husband.

'Just see what you've done, you big rascal, you careless lout! All that blood spoiling my dress! Every time you kill me it takes me a good hour to get out the stain. And you make me come back again to see all this mess! I was so happy in the next world. There, hand me a pail of water and a rag. . . . Ah, sir, excuse me, I forgot all about you. Do you know, I've brought you greetings from your late wife. Yes, I met her there; things are all topsy-turvy—she's the servant of your late man, the one you sent there, too, when you slapped him a bit too hard. The good-for-nothing had just given her a clout over her poor eye because she hadn't got all the mud off his sabots; and when his mug or his bowl don't come quick enough to suit him, he lets fly at the poor dear lady with a great kick, you know where!'

'What, my old servant? my first wife?'

The ogre turned purple, and his neck swelled like that of a turkey-cock. For fear of a rush of blood to the head the farmer blew two or three good puffs with the bellows in his face.

'That's enough, thanks. You are luckier than you deserve. That kettle you sold me so dear . . .'

'Ah, sir, mayn't you have gone at it the wrong way? Didn't you break the spell?'

'And if I broke your ribs? . . . But give me the bellows: I'm hot-blooded, and you never know when an accident will happen—I'll be just as glad to have your contraption around the house.'

'I wouldn't think of it, sir! My uncle's bellows!'

'Enough! I'll let you off everything you still owe me, and I'll give you a quarter of my sheep besides. You'll get them tonight.'

He caught up the bellows and left, still red, puffed-up, and growling—he was thinking of the way his former servant dared treat his ogress in the next world. When he entered his gateway he saw his present servant and, in a fury at the sight of him, without telling him why or wherefore, he picked up a stick, fell upon the man, and dusted him off at the seams.

'There, you scamp! You're paid in advance! Now, run to the sheepfold: take one sheep out of four, and drive them down to the farmer—a quarter of the flock.'

The ogress, who had come running when she heard the din, cried out at the top of her voice:

'A quarter of our sheep! Aren't you forgetting that you must have a good fat one every day at noon? Where will I find enough for your dinner when you eat me out of house and home, burn the candle at both ends, and throw your sheep out of the window? Give our flock to that farmer who didn't pay his due, who's laughing at you all day long with his magic kettle! You crazy fool, you greedy glut! Such sheep, so plump, so fine, so fat, so fair!'

On she went, jawing at him; she served it all up with salt and pepper. His turn next. Their voices rose; they came to high words.

To cut it short, the ogre drew his cutlass, and, beside himself, he favoured the ogress with such a stab in the gullet that she toppled over on the pavement of the courtyard. A torrent of blood spouted forth in a red river that ran under the gateway.

Here was a fine chance to try out the bellows. The ogre tried them in one nostril, then the other, blew gently, blew hard, tried it a hundred ways. It was a good hour before he understood the mishap that had befallen him. In the end he got up, eyes blazing, beard bristling, and, blowing fire through his nostrils, he set out for the farm.

At the farm the servant had delivered the sheep, and had just left after a drink or two, as was proper. Everything was set for a merry-making. They had no idea that the bellows would be tried out so soon, and they were enjoying their five-o'clock, father, mother, and children, round the table.

Suddenly one of the youngsters turned to the window.

'The ogre! Papa, it's the ogre!'

There was just time to spring to the door and bar it. But the ogre was so beside himself with fury that with a kick he knocked the door across the room. He dashed in, grabbed the farmer, who was whiter than his shirt, trying to hide under a pile of empty grain-sacks, stuffed him into one of the sacks, and hoisted the sack on his shoulders.

'Magic or no magic, get out of that now!'

He set off on the road to a pond some way off, meaning to sling the sack two or three times round his head and then let it fly into the middle of the pond.

An ogre is a tough bird. But all the rages he had flown into that day had dried up his windpipe, and the sack was heavy. After a while he had such a thirst that he stopped at the door of an inn, put down the sack, and went in to refresh himself.

The farmer, who had kept very quiet, began to move around a bit. He wriggled about, he spread his elbows, he tried to pass his hand through the top of the sack and untie the cord, but it was tied with a double knot. And the ogre would soon come back and hoist the sack on his back, to send it flying into the middle of the pond.

Suddenly the farmer felt someone push the sack with his foot, and heard a voice asking what on earth was moving in there.

By the voice he knew it was the ogre's man, but what help could he expect from that hired bully, once again as ugly tempered and twice as greedy as the ogre?

'So it's you, fellow?' he said very softly. 'Would you like to earn fifty crowns?'

'Ha, it's you, farmer? Fifty crowns, did you say?'

'Untie the cord! Listen, I've wagered a hundred against your master that he won't carry me to town without my escaping. Take my place: half of the crowns will be yours.'

The other didn't wait for him to say it twice.

As it happened, to pay off the ogre for the blows he had had from him, and as the quarter of the flock didn't come out even, he had put aside one of the sheep, and had brought it now to sell at the inn.

As soon as he had slipped the hired man into the sack the farmer retied the cord, and so tightly that you would have broken your nails on it; he put on the man's great shepherd's cape, and then, staff in hand, driving the rest of the flock, he lit out from there as if his feet were burning him. He didn't even take time to say good evening to the ogre, who was emptying bottle after bottle in the cool of the inn.

What a lot of troubles we do see! The farmer only got out of that one by the skin of his teeth. But he still felt himself in danger. Now he dared only go home at dead of night, and he started off again with his sheep at the first glimmer of dawn. All day long he kept them hidden in the bushes, on the fringe between pastures and woods.

This lasted a month or two. But all things come to an end at last. One evening when he was pasturing his flock by the steep bank of a pond he came face to face with the ogre. It was bound to happen; since the day of the sack the ogre had been scouring the country in search of his man and his flock.

'Well, sir,' said the farmer, advancing with a smile, 'are the sheep doing as well over your way as they are our way?'

The ogre stared at him; he couldn't have been more frightened if the farmer had sprouted horns.

'What? It's you, is it? Didn't I throw you down to the bottom of the pond?'

'But, sir, I was in a sack; the sack kept me from swallowing any water. And if you don't swallow any water, how can

you be drowned? Down in the pond I found another world
—just see the sheep you can get there!'

'What? you brought them back from under the water? I
would have sworn they were mine.'

'Ha, sir, at the bottom of the pond they're all over the
place. Just look there, you can see them—the ones that are
left.'

The farmer had driven the sheep to the edge of the steep
bank, and their image was reflected in the water as in a
mirror. Without a word, the ogre gazed at these sheep from
another world, his mouth wide open.

'Would you be so very kind, sir, as to put me in a sack and
throw me into the pond?' said the farmer. 'I'll go fetch the
flock we see below. There are twice as many as I've got here,
at least.'

'No,' said the ogre. 'I'll go—it's my turn. I'm so hungry
I could have swallowed all your sheep without cooking them
if I hadn't seen those down there. This last week I've grown
so thin that two of me would fit in my breeches. But now I
see sheep! Give me your staff—I'll go after them."

The trouble was that he had no sack to cover him, and he
was very much afraid of drowning.

To satisfy him, the farmer had an idea: he wrapped the
ogre in his big shepherd's cape, first making him squat down
and tying his feet together, and he tucked the hood over his
face and down his neck. This done, and well done, he gave
him a shove with all his might, and sent Sir Ogre, all tied up,
head first into the middle of the pond.

There was such a mighty splash that the sheep down below
scattered far and wide. The ogre must still be trying to call
them back, for no one since then has had any news of him
at all.

The Tale of Abbé Chanut

ONCE UPON A TIME there was a rich abbot—horribly rich; more crowns were in his coffers than he was able to count. He was called Abbé Chanut.

All the pleasure he had in life lay in bickering with his neighbours. Ah, but he was a great one for getting the best of you was the abbé! If he had had a hundred lawsuits he would have won them all. We know how that goes. It's the rich who win, every time.

Only, one fine morning, he did as the others do. Without even knowing why, he up and died.

So he went knocking at the door of Paradise.

'Tap, tap!'

'Who's there?'

'It's I—Abbé Chanut!'

'No place for you here. To hell, to hell, Abbé Chanut!'

'Who's to guide me there?'

'The rebel angel!'

Guided or not, soon he was knocking at the door of hell.

'Tap, tap!'

'Who's there?'

'It's I—Abbé Chanut!'

'Come in, come in, Abbé Chanut! Here's your place, all ready. Many's the long day it's been waiting for you.'

'Oh, what a pestiferous country! The heat's enough to kill you.'

'That's nothing at all, nothing but smoke. Come along, come along, and you'll feel the flame.'

'Wait, wait—surely I can defend myself, go to court and plead my cause? Isn't there a court of justice here?'

'A court of justice? Well, yes. . . .'

'What's it called?'

'Scratch and Claw!'

Abbé Chanut, at the top of his lungs, yelled for a lawyer. No need to go far to find one. There is no lack of lawyers in hell. Spiteful folk will even say that they all go there. That's not so, because, one fine evening, one of them did turn up in Paradise. The good Lord put him on a pitchfork and showed him to the blessed, crying, 'Here's a new kind of fruit!'

Well, let that pass. Abbé Chanut, then, lost no time in finding lawyer Cossard with whom he had done business on earth.

'Good morning to you, Master Cossard! At another time, in another place, we were good friends. Couldn't you do me a bit of a favour, in exchange for a bit of cash, of course?'

On earth people love money so much that in hell they must still love it—perhaps even more.

'Couldn't you write a letter that I could hand in to the Board of Control?'

'Why, of course!'

Lawyer Cossard took down a few notes, wrote the letter. And Abbé Chanut, on the pretext that he must take it to the Board of Control, was given permission to leave hell.

When he reached the gates of hell there was a fearsome devil on guard, but he was hung up above the gate by his four paws. 'If I hadn't been tied so tight,' cried the devil to

Abbé Chanut, 'I'd have swallowed you in two gulps!' No use: he was held fast by his iron chains and couldn't get free until Easter should fall in a blue moon.

So there was Abbé Chanut, out again on the high-road. Round a bend in the road he ran into good Saint Just. 'Where are you going, good Saint Just?'

'To Paradise.'

'To Paradise! Ah, there's a lovely word. Couldn't you do me a bit of a favour? In exchange for a bit of cash, of course. I was only wondering if you could take me along under your cloak.'

'That *is* annoying,' said good Saint Just to himself. . . . 'Take Abbé Chanut under my cloak? . . . Abbé Chanut!' But good Saint Just was so kind and easy-going that in the end he took Abbé Chanut along, and slipped him in under his cloak, right beneath the nose of Saint Peter.

As soon as he was in Paradise Abbé Chanut came out from under the cloak. Oho! the cries that went up as soon as he showed himself. 'Outside, Abbé Chanut! To hell, to hell!'

Abbé Chanut ran to find the good Lord.

'My Lord, you have said that he who shall come into your Paradise, nevermore shall he leave it. Lord, just for one man don't make yourself out a liar!'

He stayed there.

But this is the reason that since that day neither cloak nor shirt is allowed to enter Paradise. No one comes in who is not pure and unadorned.

The Tale of Belle-Rose

ONCE UPON A TIME there was a poor man, a peasant, so poor that, as the saying goes, he owed money to dog and wolf at once. He had not so much as a good Sunday coat to wear when he went to town. And so he never went there.

At last, by dint of working with a stout heart, digging and delving, he put a few pennies aside, paid his debts, and got on his feet again. When autumn came there was a calf to be sold. The day of the yearly fair he left for town, shabby as he was.

Before leaving he inquired as to what errands the household wanted done. He had three daughters, Marguerite, Violette, and Rose, his three flowers, he called them, and dearly he loved all three. But his heart leaned to the youngest because she was of good courage, like himself, never putting herself forward, blithe and easy to please; she found everything good that came her way. She was good to look at and good to be with; all who knew her were wont to sing her the old song:

> Fairest rose, whitest rose,
> Lovely rose of spring!

Said he, standing before the door with the calf's rope in his hand, 'It's a long time since I've been to the fair; what can I bring you all?'

And Marguerite said, 'A fine dress, colour of the moon.'

And Violette said, 'A fine dress, colour of the sun.'

And Belle-Rose said nothing.

'And you, my dear one, what can I bring you from town? A fine dress, silver or gold, like your sisters?'

Rose cared little for finery; what was on her mind was that she must churn the milk for butter and then set the curds for cheese.

'Come now, tell me, dear child.'

'Father, there is nothing I want.'

'I'll not leave until you tell me.'

'Well then, father, since I am called Rose, bring me back a rose.'

She had spoken without remembering that summer was past, and roses were gone with it. But the father remembered and it was on his mind all the way. 'Maybe,' he thought, 'I'll see a rose in town, in some rich burgher's garden.'

When he had sold his calf he managed to find the two dresses, the moon-coloured and the sun-coloured. And he would have given much of his money to find one, but no rose could he see. So he had to leave for home with none.

By this time the sky was overcast, clouds rose, and the wind sprang up. Snow began to fall in great flakes. The poor man found it hard walking; he had lingered too long in search of his rose. Night drew on. He tried to cut across the heath, and lost his way.

On and on he walked, until he was drenched and could go no farther. All about him stretched a country which he had never seen before—ponds, copses, and moors. Foremost in his mind was his chagrin that he must come back without a rose for his youngest, while the two others had what they desired. Then suddenly it came to him, 'My wife and the girls will think that thieves have stopped me on the highway, and that to have my purse they had first to take my life. . . . Besides, I may well lose it—I can no longer tell where I am. . . . I am weary enough to drop in my tracks. A moment more and I am like to fall down in the snow and the breath leave my body.'

Just when he was losing all hope, wet, benumbed, and forspent, through the snow that flew like a swarm of bees he saw a light. He took courage, gathered his forces, and went on. Soon he came to a castle, all brightly lit.

The great portal was wide open. The poor man was none too bold; he hesitated. But needs must, he could do no other. Either he must go in, or fall down where he stood.

He entered the courtyard and climbed the steps. All the doors stood open. And yet there was no one in sight: how strange! He called, softly, then louder: no answer. He took three steps forward, ready to swoon with cold and hunger. In the hall before him there was a great fire, and a table all laid; he went towards them. Soup was steaming in the tureen. He ventured to sit down and serve himself a ladleful. 'If I eat I shall feel bolder.' He poured a glass of wine in his broth. Taking heart, he attacked a roast chicken whose savoury odour mounted to his nostrils, and ate whatever else lay before him, jellied ham and a pear tart—he even emptied the bottle.

After this he felt himself another man, and dared enter the next room. He stripped off his clothes, already half dry, spread them before the fire and betook himself to bed—a feather bed, with a warm down coverlet—and, without troubling his head any longer over there being no one in sight, he fell asleep.

His sleep was sound that night. In the morning, when he had dressed, he looked about for someone to whom he might offer his excuses and his thanks. And not a living soul could he find.

Not knowing what to think of what had befallen him, he decided to leave. . . . And there, growing by the portal, he saw a rose-bush—and, despite last night's snowfall, it had just bloomed. Yes, it was covered with roses in bud or barely open, as round and red as Easter eggs.

Again he hesitated. But the rose was so tempting! Must he come back empty-handed to his youngest, and to her alone, when there before him was the very thing she had asked of him? The strangeness of the spot was enough to put him on his guard. On the other hand, he could see himself giving the rose to his dear Rose, and telling her of his adventures. Finally he could stand it no longer; choosing the loveliest of the flowers, he drew his knife and cut it.

Oh, but it was an unwise thing that he was doing! What trouble he was stirring up for himself, poor man!

By the rose-bush, as though he had sprung from the earth, appeared a Beast. So ugly was he to see, so fit to inspire disgust and fright, that the man dropped the knife. Muzzle like that of a great mastiff, paws like those of a lizard, body and tail like those of that fearsome beast spotted with yellow who lives in holes under mossy places—a salamander.

'You came into my castle,' said this Beast, 'you ate and drank well, you dried yourself and slept warm. And, for all your thanks, when you leave, you cut the finest of my flowers! Wretch, your last hour has come!'

With slavering jaws, the Beast advanced upon the man, who drew back tembling. Hardly knowing what he said, he admitted his wrong-doing, and offered to buy the rose—to give the Beast his purse, or anything he wished.

'You are talking in the air,' said the Beast. 'Have you daughters?'

'I have three; I cut the rose for the one called Belle-Rose.'

'Listen, then: in a week from this very day, if you are not prepared to pay yourself, let one of your three daughters come here, to be mine. Do you hear?'

223

'Yes, I hear.'

'Since you have cut the rose, take it. When your daughter comes, let her cut another—I shall appear. Afterwards, let her do—if she is wise enough—what will be expected of her.'

There was no use in pleading. In any case, the Beast had disappeared. All the poor man could do was to start for home.

He started on his way, sorely troubled in mind. 'This Beast, what does he want of my daughter? What will he do with my child, my little girl?'

He did not even ask himself which daughter would go to the Beast's castle: he knew that already. Among his three flowers he knew which one bore blooms of courage and devotion, just as on a rose-bush are found only roses. And he gave a great shudder as he journeyed along. Snow melting on the branches dripped down his neck, and he did not know it was snow; he stumbled over pebbles and did not know they were pebbles; he frightened away linnets from bushes and did not know they were linnets. His mind kept dwelling on the minute when the frightful beast had appeared, and on the terrible words he had spoken. 'What does he want of my daughter? What will he do with my daughter?'

At last he reached his home, pale and shaken, the whites of his eyes yellow with fear, stooping as though he were ten years older. His wife and daughters thought it was just fatigue, that he was done in after his night on the moors. They pleaded with him to eat a bite, but he would have nothing but a glass of cold water. So he sat there, before the fire.

Marguerite and Violette did not fail to ask if he had brought them dresses like the sun and moon. He took them out of his sack.

'To you, my poor Rose, I bring the rose which you asked of me. But it will cost us dearer than the fine clothes of your sisters!'

And then he told them what had befallen him.

'And, to make an end, this Beast told me that he would come after me and devour me if, by a week from today, I have not brought him one of my three daughters.'

No one spoke. All that could be heard in the room was the crackling of the fire on the hearth.

'Never,' said Marguerite, 'could I set foot in that castle my father told about, where everything is done but no one can be seen.'

'At the very idea,' said Violette, 'of that Beast who would appear I should fall down dead on the road. Oh, why must Rose have made that fatal wish?'

'Ha, yes!' went on Marguerite, 'look at the sorrow she has brought on our father!'

'I will be the one to go to the castle,' said Rose, unable to hold back her tears. 'You are hard of heart to reproach me with it, but it is true: through me sorrow and anguish have come upon my father. When the hour of reckoning comes I will go to the Beast.'

The seven days went by, slowly and yet so fast! in a house of mourning, in a house of tears. . . .

The day came when Rose set out with her father on the road to the castle. As he retraced his steps he stumbled over the same pebbles, caught his clothes on the same bushes, all because of the same thoughts that tormented his mind. 'What will he do with my daughter, that Beast? He will have our Rose at his will. Belle-Rose, my tall girl, my good girl, who brought me my bowl of soup at noon, to the field where I was ploughing. Last summer when I cut the wheat she was close behind me, tying up the sheaves. I shall turn to look for her, but never again shall I see her eyes laughing at me. Ha, evenings, when I hear the boys singing along the road,

> "Fairest rose, whitest rose,
> Lovely rose of spring!"

. . . I shall feel the heart leaving my body.'

Walking in silence, they came to the Beast's castle. They went into the court. Doors all open, tables laid, even steam rising from the soup tureen. But Rose went straight to the great rose-bush, and there she picked a rose.

Immediately the Beast appeared—great red eyes standing out of his head, muzzle dripping with slobber, skin as wrinkled as a turkey's neck, and slimy as that of a frog. So grim and fearsome to see that poor Rose trembled all over her body.

And yet the Beast's eyes were soft and pleading. And he spoke gently, you might almost say in friendly fashion.

'Is it you, Belle-Rose?'

'Yes. . . . I am Rose.'

'Have no fear if there are things in my castle that surprise you. Would there might be a greater surprise for you some day. Rose, all that is here is for your use. Just as your father spent his night here, you will spend your time as you will. You might even find happiness for all your life long if you but knew how to grasp it. . . . Listen, now—when you wish to speak to me you must pluck a rose.'

At that the Beast sighed and disappeared.

Rose and her father spent three days together in the castle. They saw nobody, but the table was always set for them, the beds made. Three times a day the bell rang, and they found whatever they wished to eat ready upon the table. But their minds were not on their food. They lived the life of the castle, far better than in their poor house, and yet they wanted nothing more than to be back home, without the thought of separation that lay like a weight on their hearts.

Nevertheless the father had to leave. Rose even pressed him to do so, thinking of her mother. He left, and went back to guiding the plough behind his oxen. And, as he went, he still did not know how he could leave his Rose with the Beast.

'The Beast spoke softly, but perhaps he has a black, lying throat. And what did he mean with his strange words? Yes, what does he want of my daughter? My child, the child I christened, whom I had to leave in his power? Ha, well I know that in Rose's eyes you can see her angel, who is always with her. But even if the Beast is not all a brute will he be able to see Rose's angel? Will he know that she is all goodness, all sunshine?'

So he thought on his way back across the fields, and there were moments when his heart was less heavy.

Rose had gone with him as far as the outer portal. Then she went back to the rose-bush, which sprang up there by the entry, as though it were the secret and soul of the castle. Reverently she cut a rose.

Straightway the Beast appeared.

If only, Rose thought, the Beast could make her understand what he wanted of her! When she saw his eyes, and heard his voice, she felt compassion for him. She could not have touched him, but she did wish that she might help him in his trouble.

The Beast saw that she was full of good-will, kind and pure and good. And her beauty shone the brighter in this glow.

'I thank you for giving shelter to my father before I let him leave,' said Rose. 'I will show you all the courtesy that is in my power.'

'Rose, what you say, does it come from your heart? How kind you are not to be repelled by my ugliness, oh beautiful Rose!'

The Beast was lying at her feet, beside the rose-bush, and looked at her mildly, his eyes on hers. He went on speaking, and what he said was so tender, so sad, that Rose felt drawn to him.

'I know what I am, what I have well deserved to be: a Beast framed for horror and loathing, who must cause you to shudder far more than a spider or a toad. And yet, Rose, my

Rose, you have compassion on me! If only you could guess.
. . . But if I say more all hope is gone.'

The Beast gazed at her, sighing and groaning, tears running from his eyes. A malicious soul would have laughed at him. But Rose, though she felt like shuddering, gave him back his look of friendship, and found the right words to soften his misery. She promised him that his presence would never be distasteful to her, and that she would be his friend.

'Come what may, I shall not abandon you.'

'Hear me, Rose—I put my faith in you. Soon I shall give you three days in which to go and see your father and mother. But the third day, will you promise me to come back?'

'Dear God,' said Rose to herself, 'what is in store for me? Not only am I prisoner in this castle, bound by my word, but now I am bound by friendship for the Beast. When I heard his complaint, I could not help myself. When he looks at me, there is such distress in his eyes. Surely there is a secret he cannot tell me. And I, I cannot guess it.'

The pity in her was so strong that she longed to leave for a while. She reminded the Beast of the promise he had made her, that he would let her spend three days at her home.

'All those three days I shall be grieving for you, my Rose,' said the Beast. 'When I no longer feel you near me, or your eyes upon me, I shall wither like the hay, which is mown and dries upon the earth. Go, then, since you must: I trust you, that your return will be prompt. I am risking my own misfortune, but I put myself in your hands. If you only knew the power that is yours, and the faith that is mine. . . .'

When Rose appeared at the door of her house, what a joyful surprise for her family! They ran to embrace her, as though they had thought they would never see her again. And she, poor girl, she asked their pardon for all the sorrow she had brought on them.

They questioned her, though scarcely daring to, about life

at the castle. That is, about the Beast. She said that she felt he wished her no harm: that he looked at her as would a person, that she thought him deserving of anyone's affection.

Three days went quickly by, and they made as much of her as they could. The parents were easier in their minds: from what Rose had said, the Beast had no harm in him. Only, once their fears were relieved, they no longer wanted to let her go back.

They pressed her so, with prayers and persuasions, that she spent another night at the house. She should have left betimes next morning for the castle, but they found a thousand excuses to keep her; it was afternoon before she was able to start on her way.

Towards nightfall she reached the Beast's castle. All along the road she had made haste, for her heart was full of foreboding, and even heavy with remorse. Swiftly she ran, almost flew, past ponds and copses, thinking only of the misfortune which would follow her least delay.

And what did she see? There by the doorway, the great rose-bush, the soul of the place, seemed already withered, as though touched by frost.

She felt the blow in her heart. For the rose-bush stood for love, and love had been tried and found wanting. Was not its withering a proof of this? The roses had shed their petals, all save one. This last one Rose cut, in great haste.

But the Beast did not appear.

She stood there all trembling. A faint rustling reached her ears, as though someone was trying to lift himself, groaning. She took a few steps towards the foot of the garden, and there the groans sounded more clearly. She went in that direction, and, near the fountain and its pool, she saw the Beast.

And in a far worse plight than was the rose-bush. He lay there swooning, at the point of death, ready to fall back beneath the ferns in the pool from which he had just risen.

There was no strength in him, and very little life.

'I have come to pray you for pardon,' said Rose.

'Rose! Ah, Rose,' said the Beast, 'you see that I die because of you.'

'Do not doubt me, you have no cause. . . . And do wish me no harm.'

'Rose, I wish you no harm, but you see what I am come to by your delay. Do you not know that my heart is yours, and that far from your eyes I can no longer live?'

'Beast, my Beast,' said Rose. 'I am here.'

Her heart was so full, so burning with compassion, that there was no room in it for fear or disgust. Seeing that the Beast was all bemired she bent over and took him in her arms, to wash him at the fountain.

And oh, most wonderful to see! No sooner had she touched him with her gentle hands, no sooner had she performed this gracious act of love, than she saw before her, no longer the Beast, but a boy who could only be a king's son, a prince bright as the day. Rose found him so beautiful that she was struck dumb.

'Rose,' said the prince, kneeling before her. 'I had well deserved that an evil fate should befall me. All I could think of was revelry and battles; nothing did I know of pity and charity. Beggars disgusted me, with their rags and their sores. One day, when I mocked at a poor man who asked for bread at the door, I beheld myself changed into a Beast. My castle was to remain open to every passer-by, and to offer him food and lodging, while I was to live in a hole in the earth. But before the door was to be a rose-bush, as a sign of love; the first rose that bloomed was to be brought to a fair maiden who was daughter to a poor man; she must then agree to come, and at the last her heart must turn in love to the Beast; a day must come when she would touch him of her own accord, without his asking it, and without shuddering. Then the spell would be broken. If this had not come to pass I should have died in the shape of a Beast, and the fair maid, whose heart was not open to compassion, would have died too.'

But there was no need of so many words. Without a thought of dying, Belle-Rose was as radiant as himself.

Hand in hand they went back to the rose-bush. It had grown green again, and was full of blooms, as a sign that love had fulfilled itself. The rose-bush was saying, was singing, that Belle-Rose and the Beast, the prince of the castle and the poor man's daughter, were to be joined as man and wife.

Her father, mother, and sisters all came for the wedding, and Rose kept them with her thereafter. And for all poor folk the castle remained a place of welcome.

And all through the lives of Belle-Rose and her prince the great rose-bush near the doorway went on blooming, as a tree for all who love, rose upon rose.

The Tale of Comme Ça

ONCE UPON A TIME there were two countrymen who had known each other when they were boys and apprenticed to a miller. A few years later they met by chance at a fair.

'Why, it's you, think of that! It's a long time. . . . Well, how are you?'

'Oh, *comme ça*. Since I saw you, bless me, I got married.'

'Well, that's good news.'

'Oh, *comme ça*. The wife I chose, I'd hardly say she was a good wife.'

'That's too bad. It can't be much fun.'

'Oh, *comme ça*. She brought me three thousand crowns in ready money.'

'Well, hang it! That's a consolation.'

'Oh, *comme ça*. I put the money into sheep. The pox came along and the whole flock died before my eyes.'

'What a misfortune! No need to ask if you're sorry for yourself.'

'Oh, *comme ça*. It turned out the skins sold well, almost better than I'd have got for them on the hoof.'

'So, then, you got your money's worth?'

'Oh, *comme ça*. I took it and bought a house with it.'

'Well, but the pox won't carry *that* off! A house, that'll last.'

'Oh, *comme ça*. Last week the house burned down.'

'Alas, my poor friend! That *is* a calamity!'

'Oh, *comme ça*. My wife was in the house and she burned too.'

The Tale of Some Bad News

ONCE UPON A TIME there was a man and his wife who owned a cow. The day after Christmas the cow up and died. Right away the woman was after the man to buy another one, and she carried on so that in the end he gave in. It was to be done at Candlemas. He went to town for the holiday fair, and he had promised to bring back the cow before evening.

Afternoon went by. The clock struck four, and then five. The good woman sat by her window, watching and knitting. But, like sister Anne, she saw only the road all dust and the grass growing green. She was waiting for the man to appear, leading his cow by a rope—and nothing came in sight.

At last, however, she saw a man. He was on his way, but he led no cow. And it was not her husband, but a man from the village below.

She went to the door. Still a long way off, he waved at her. She was all of a fret.

When he arrived he was panting, trying to catch his breath.

'Ha, poor Marion, the news I bring you isn't too good. . . .'

'Ah, my God. . . .'

'Yes. Your man was bringing back a cow he had bought at the fair . . .'

'And then?'

'Then, well—he let her get loose.'

'What a shame!'

'Wait, now. He ran after her, and he caught her.'

'Ah, well, that's good.'

'Wait, wait! The cow struggled. They were on the foot-bridge—the planks were wet and slippery underfoot—the cow fell in the stream.'

'Oh, what a calamity!'

'But wait. Your man hadn't let go the cord . . .'

'Ah, that's good.'

'And he fell in too. The water was high, and they were both swept away.'

'Even the cow?'

'The cow was carried as far as from here to the fountain. Your man perhaps twice as far.'

'They got the cow out?'

'They got both of them out. Only, poor Marion . . .'

'Oh, tell me quickly, mercy on us! The cow is dead?'

'No, but your poor man, when they took him out of the water, it was already too late. Drowned: yes, drowned dead. There they are, coming with the stretcher. They're bringing him back to you.'

'Yes, but my cow?'

'Oh, they're bringing her along. She climbed out on the bank.'

'Thanks be to God! Then my man's dead?'

'Ah, yes.'

'But there's nothing wrong with the cow?'

'Ah, no.'

'Well, with the way you have of telling things, neighbour, you can boast that you gave me a fine fright!'

The Tale of the White Rat

ONCE UPON A TIME there was a king in a country at the other end of the world. And he was married but he had no children. For lack of children he and his wife had set their affections on a white rat.

What a miracle they made her out to be, that white rat! How they did go on about her pretty ways and tricks and graces! There was nothing to equal their white rat in all their kingdom and in all the kingdoms of the earth.

One day they even went to see the queen of the fairies, to beg her to change their white rat into a human being.

The queen of the fairies must have been under obligations to them—one good turn deserves another among fairies and kings and queens—and she granted their wish.

As a usual thing fairies change kings' sons and daughters into a blue bird, if it's not into a more fantastic beast. This time it was the other way around—an even more remarkable prodigy. There was the white rat, turned into a princess, a princess all lightness and grace. All you could say was that her eyes were just a wee bit pink, her little face a wee bit pointed.

To tell the truth, the good folk of the country grumbled

about it. They said, although not too loud, for fear of the king's men, that a dog will never learn to purr, a sheep that lives in a castle still smells like a sheep, and twenty other proverbs to show that no one can change his skin.

Blood will tell in the end.

A day came when the king thought that it was time for him to do like all the other kings—that is, marry off his daughter in the highest nobility.

'Time to marry you, my love, my lambkin! Tell me you are willing.'

'Quite willing, father. But who is it you're giving me for a husband?'

'Whoever you wish, my daughter, whoever you wish.'

'Father, I want the most powerful husband that can be found in the world.'

And that was talking.

The king thought it over for three days. At the end of those three days he said to himself that the most powerful being in the world must surely be the sun.

The sun drives away winter, cold, and night. He makes the grass grow, the leaves and fruit, the grains that sustain animal life; every living creature draws life from him first of all.

The king went to tell the princess that he was going to ask for the sun as a bridegroom for her.

The princess made a face.

'The sun? But he is not the most powerful being in the world! Only one cloud, that's enough! The cloud covers him like a mask, puts out his light—no more sun! All that is left is fog and shadow over the earth. I want something better than old Father Sun.'

The king went away and thought for three more days. Then he came back to tell his daughter that he would ask for the cloud as a bridegroom for her, the cloud that fills all space and covers whole kingdoms.

The Tale of the White Rat

The princess made a face.

'The cloud? But just let the wind come up: the wind drives him about, tears him to tatters, sweeps him away and blows him into the far corners of the sky. No more cloud is left. No, no, I want something better than old Father Cloud!'

The king went away and thought for three days. Then he came back to tell his daughter that he would ask for the wind as a bridegroom for her, the wind who drives all before him and who can rule the sea.

The princess made a face.

'The wind? Easy enough to get out of the wind's power: all you need do is shelter yourself behind a wall, behind a mountain. Even though he bows down the tall trees and uproots the oaks, what can he do against the mountain, that mass of earth and rocks? No, no, for myself I want something better than old Father Wind!'

The king went away and thought for three days. Then he came back to tell his daughter that he would ask for the mountain as a bridegroom for her, the mountain that withstands the tempests, that the lightning strikes and cannot move.

The princess made a face.

'The mountain? But there is one who is more powerful than the mountain. It is he who gnaws at it, with a tooth sharper than a needle, eats it away, tunnels roads in it, lives in it as though it were a cheese, and makes his castle of it as he pleases. There is someone greater than the sun, the cloud, the wind, greater than the mountain. There is the rat, the mountain-slasher, the rat, with pointed teeth, so handsome, so brave, the marvel of marvels, more powerful than any being that can be imagined in this poor world—in a word, the Rat!'

Well, yes, there it was in a nutshell.

The princess knew what she wanted. She knew it so well that the king and queen had to go and find the queen of the fairies and beg her on their bended knees to change the princess back into a white rat.

The fairy did it with her wand.

And then the marriage was held of the white lady rat and a big bald he-rat with a tail a foot long.

> His tail's one,
>   Her tail's two,
> This tale's three,
>   And now we're through.

THE END